73858

BIOGRAPHY Beattie, Jessie Louise, 1896-
Beatt   A season past; reminiscences of a rural
        Canadian childhood. Toronto, McClelland and
        Stewart, 1968.
        153 p.

        I. Title.

                             60107

                                6

A Season Past
Reminiscences of a Rural Canadian Childhood

A Season Past

Reminiscences of a Rural Canadian Childhood

Jessie L. Beattie

McClelland and Stewart Limited  Toronto/Montreal

❧ To the Memory of a Happy Childhood ❧

❧ Characters in this Book ❧

My parents and our family, including me.
Those who came and went along the road.

DESIGN AND ILLUSTRATIONS: GORDON OGLAN

The Canadian Publishers
McClelland and Stewart Limited
25 Hollinger Road, Toronto 16

PRINTED AND BOUND IN CANADA

❧ Also by Jessie L. Beattie ❧

NOVELS

Hill Top
Three Measures
The Split in the Sky
Strength for the Bridge

BIOGRAPHIES

John Christie Holland
Black Moses

TRAVEL

White Wings Around the World

SHORT STORIES

Hasten the Day

SKETCHES

Along the Road

POETRY

Blown Leaves
Shifting Sails

❦ Contents ❧

"Come here, my girl," said my father in a voice of suppressed excitement.

He sat by a small table; I on a stool across the room from him in the parlour of the old farm house. On the table were stacks of neatly laid bank notes and shining mounds of silver that sprawled into an irregular mountain range. Before him was a sheet of paper on which he had jotted a vertical column of figures.

It was an October afternoon. The grain harvest had been garnered and threshed, the root crops had been lifted, the winter celery stood firmly replanted in the dark cool earth of the storage pit, the apples were barrelled in the cellar. My father was recording the profits of a year's labour.

I went eagerly to him. He gathered up the notes, one pile upon another, and tied them neatly with a cord. Then he cupped his big hands around the stack and held it out to me. "No, no," he said, when I tried to take it from him; "put your hands side by side."

I did so and he placed the assembled riches on them. "Now," he said, "when you grow up, you can tell your children that you once held pretty close to a thousand dollars when you were just a little girl." In those days, this was a considerable sum of money.

He returned the bank notes to the table, drew a firm stroke with his pencil below the vertical row of figures and began to add. Once or twice he glanced toward the window with its panel of heavy marquisette on which my sister Jean had stencilled a border of red tulips. I had tried unsuccessfully to peer through the thick mesh of threads many times but of course the eyes of a thief would be sharper than mine!

Once Mother opened the parlour door a crack and

ventured, "How are you getting on, Frank?"

"Ninety-one, ninety-six, one hundred, one hundred and. . . ." He paused, frowning, pencil suspended, and waved her out. "You made me lose count, then," he chided. "I'll send for you when I've finished."

A thousand dollars! And many a time there had been less than a hundred left, my father said, after all was paid. Now he could buy the dogskin coat for Mother which he had promised her for Christmas and one for himself too.

That was the year he turned fifty and began to put on weight. He had always been tall and slim and Mother complained that he didn't look natural. She blamed the change on his increasing fondness for bananas and buttermilk; but I don't think that had anything to do with it.

I believe that his noticeable gain in avoirdupois was the result of improved conditions in the family, coupled with a sense of financial security. The final mortgage payment had been made, a new barn and an up-to-date pen for the thoroughbred Tamworths had been built. The farm house was now serviced with a water system. The spring of supply was almost a quarter of a mile away, but a crystal clear drink could be had by turning a tap in the kitchen. Other comforts had been added and our family was enjoying the longest period of good health on record.

My father still rose with the sun and was on the go until darkness fell. Winter, after the middle of January, remained the busiest season of the year for him; seed-planting in the greenhouses did not start until February but great fires had to be kept on for weeks in advance of that date to thaw out the very foundations of the buildings and to warm the mixture of soils he stored in autumn in preparation for sowing. Pine roots from partly cleared land were hauled by sleigh and stacked outside the greenhouses, cheap fuel for the furnaces. After a strike or two of the axe laid their great dark hulks open, a sweetish spicy smell rose from the pale orange of the unnourished wood.

3

If winter winds were high, and when the temperature fell to below zero, my father watched the fires all night long while they crackled and sparked, sending belches of dense smoke, lit by minute red stars, from the tall brick chimneys into the whirling air.

But although the "hot houses", as we called them, kept my father busier than most men during the winter months, he found time for winter fairs, farmers' conventions, church conferences, country sales, visits to friends and relatives, and, with the first fall of snow, a day of hunting in the Puslinch highlands.

Winter was the season, too, when country people lingered over meals and drew their chairs around the fire to talk of old times and to predict the future. Thereby many a knotty problem was solved, many an important decision reached. There were conversions and controversies, the breaking down of prejudices and the building of friendships.

My father was a religious man but he was not denomination-bound. He was patriotic but not partisan, he lived a moral life yet understood temptation and did not condemn. Therefore he drew his friends from many walks of life. A Liberal in politics, his best friend was a staunch Conservative. He was a farmer without a college degree, but one of his most frequent visitors, who sat talking with him far into the night, was a university professor.

His was a common round, but he escaped from it by means of imagination and was never bored with life. He had dreamed, as a boy, of becoming a great inventor, but harnessed his dream, as an adult, to creating simple toys for us and for the children of neighbours and relatives. He made sleds and stilts, jacks-in-boxes and dolls.

Perhaps his finest model was a doll carved from a maple stick with legs and arms that moved by some concealed wire mechanism, and a platinum wig fashioned from the clipped hide of a sheep. When Mother complained that she looked pale, my father brought her chiselled features alive with the

4

paintbrush which had decorated many a carriage with sprigs of flowers and other fancy designs.

For my father had many skills. As well as carriage-maker, he had been miller, carpenter, blacksmith and lumber-man in his pioneer days. Now working with wood was his favourite hobby and he brought his work into the kitchen when his workshop became too cold, unashamedly leaving a litter of woody curls and shavings for Mother to sweep into the dust-pan.

Watching him as he shaped a doll's cradle for me, "You'd better go up to the North Pole and be a helper to Santa Claus," my Uncle John said.

Uncle John was my father's brother. His long-fingered white hands were never used for manual work.

There were some who did not appreciate my father.

My father was a blunt man but his criticisms were never barbed. He thought before he spoke, his remarks were well-intentioned and his purpose was right, therefore few who understood his nature were offended by his frankness. There was, for instance, the case of Orison Howe.

∿［ The House of Howe ］∿

My father had brown hair and brown eyes and wore a beard, but Orison Howe had small blue eyes in a face that narrowed to the mouth, and had almost no chin, and no beard at all.

Orison Howe owned a dairy farm with a large herd of Holsteins, so large that he rented extra pasture land from his neighbour. He raised his own stock and was an expert in choice and quantity of feed. My father said he had never known Orison to have a sick cow nor to lose a calf. The Howe barns and stables were imposing and well-designed, but the house was queer, built like a mill, tall and straight and full of windows, set high above a stream and with no front door. It had the look of not being lived in. There were neither shrubs nor flowers around it. The roof was patched and lacked a proper cornice.

"Orison has been intending to reshingle his house for the past ten years," my father said, one day. "If he keeps on repairing at the rate he's been going lately, it won't cost him much to cover what's left."

Orison kept his family of seven boys and five girls with their noses to the grindstone. The youngest, twin boys, were seven about the time I made their acquaintance. They were tall and thin like their father and so alike that it was impossible for anyone but their mother to tell one from the other.

As the older children grew to maturity, they took matters in their own hands and, one by one, they drifted off to make happier lives for themselves. One ran away, another left in a temper and his parents had no notion of where he went. Orison did not understand that it was he who had failed as a father, but instead blamed the waywardness of his family on the early character of Mrs. Howe, who had run away from home to marry him. He confided this to my

7

father in a loud whisper, one day, when they met on the road, each with a load of bagged grain, one going and one returning from the grist. I was with my father.

Orison's whispered confidences sounded exciting to my small ears, and I could hardly wait to make the acquaintance of Mrs. Howe. But when I did so, I was bitterly disappointed. She was a dull plain woman without a spark of romance about her. I did not realize then that such a quality may be lost with the passing of years, especially when passed in the company of a man like Orison Howe.

My father said that there was nothing mean nor base about the man. He was just uncomprehending. A hard worker himself without a conscious need for change who had never thought of taking a vacation, he didn't appreciate that young people in the country wanted to keep pace with the altering pattern of living elsewhere.

On communion Sundays, Orison wore the same blue broadcloth suit in which he had been married. It was a good-looking suit still and much better pressed than my father's, and it got less wear; none of the Howe children rode to church astride their father's knee. There was no visible show of affection in the Howe family.

We became acquainted with the Howes through John Allison, a butcher in Galt. My father was a regular customer of Mr. Allison's, who stopped in to see us when he came our way, cattle-buying. Occasionally, my father joined him in the role of guide to farmers who had stock fat enough to sell, and it was on one such expedition that they called at the Howe farm.

Orison was busy in the cellar, picking over potatoes, with the twins and two other children helping him. My father said the young ones were skimpily clad and should have been at school, but Orison explained that they all had bad colds and that he would be glad when the winter was over.

My father and the butcher were invited to stay for dinner and, although there was plenty to eat, the sparing supply of butter and the lack of milk for the children had been noted; for them the beef stew had consisted mostly of gravy.

"The bread was store bread, that sticky stuff that goes into a gooey ball in the mouth," my father said as he reached for a slice of Mother's wheaten loaf, that night at supper. "Mrs. Howe ought to know how to bake or set her children to do it. And what's wrong with Orison? He's an expert at feeding cattle. He says that his folks were pioneers from Scotland. That being the case, he was most likely raised on oatmeal and fat pork and rubbed with goose grease. I'd like to speak to the man but we're not well enough acquainted for me to be sure that he cares more for his family than he does about being in the right."

So began an unusual friendship between two men who were poles apart in point-of-view and personality. Whether my father ventured to advise Orison Howe as to the value of foods, I don't know, but by the time I was old enough to interest myself in the conversation of adults, the Howes were regular winter visitors to our house and occasionally we went to see them.

Mrs. Howe, small, faded, uncommunicative, had graying hair and always wore gray dresses – print, at home, and poplin for church and visiting. Her eyes were gray and still, her skin drab and unhealthy looking, the nails of her hands were flat and colourless. She spoke in a monotone and usually in agreement. "Yes, yes . . ." and again, "yes, yes."

"Do you think she's a bit deaf and doesn't want anybody to know?" wondered my father.

"No, no," Mother explained. "She's just lost interest."

There was one visit of the Howe's which we had good reason to remember.

"Orison never takes a holiday," my father remarked one winter evening after returning from a day of cattle-buying with John Allison. "We called in today and I spoke about the Fat Stock Show coming off soon. Orison's been specializing in dairy cattle for years, gets top prices for his

9

cream and milk, but he's never shown a beast nor been to a fair. He admitted it today. He's afraid of losing time and dying poor. The man's poor now with a day-to-day poorness that is affecting everybody in that home. He's like a machine that's never been shut down for oiling. He hasn't enough give to him. I've asked him to go with me to the Show at Guelph. He said he'd think it over."

"If he decides to go," Mother replied, "tell him to bring Mrs. Howe along to spend the day with me. She needs a change as much as he does. The last time I saw her was at Wilkinson's. She was buying underwear for the older twins. She had hardly a word to say to me and she was worried looking."

"Well, can you wonder? They haven't heard anything from Ronnie and it's going on six months."

Ronnie had been the oldest of the boys remaining at home. He had walked off during haying time, on his eighteenth birthday, after informing his father that he was a man now and expected to be paid wages.

"They had words over it," my father said, "and Orison told him he still had a few years to work out his keep from when he was born – that it would be time enough to talk wages when he was twenty-one. Ronnie stuck his fork in a coil of hay and left. Orison thought he'd gone in a temper and that he'd come back but he hasn't."

"He'll lose them all, I'm afraid," Mother predicted. "He has no tact with them and no understanding. The house has been allowed to go to rack and ruin. He seems free enough with money when it comes to building stables but it must be years since he's spent anything on making that house a home for his children. Yes, I'm afraid he'll lose them all."

"Unless something sharp happens to waken him up," my father answered.

On the morning of the Fair, the Howes arrived at our farm before six o'clock when we were still at breakfast. Mother gave her place at the table to Mrs. Howe and poured

10

her a cup of coffee. Orison drank one standing. He refused a chair and nervously moved from one foot to the other.

The distance to Guelph was seventeen miles. Snow was falling.

"Don't try to make the trip both ways today. If the snowing keeps up the roads will be heavy," Mother warned. "You'll be welcome and quite comfortable either at Cousin Gilbert's or at Peter Beattie's. They always expect company at Fair time. There'll be no need to drive home tonight." Gilbert and Peter were relatives on my father's side of the family.

Orison set his coffee cup on the table with a suddenness which made us all look at him. "I think I'd better take my own cutter, Frank," he said. "I can't spare more than a day. I've too much work to do."

My father nodded. "Don't worry. If you must get home, we'll get back tonight but it may be late. Leave your horse and cutter here as we planned. There's no pleasure nor wisdom in driving seventeen miles alone."

My brother had taken the Howe horse to the barn and had run the cutter under the stable shed. He was already bringing Prince, harnessed and prancing, toward the driving-shed in which our cutter waited.

We watched from the window as my father and his friend hurried out. The sun was streaking the east with rose but the sky was heavily clouded. The glass panes were chased with leaves of frost, the falling snow was crisp and sparkling, gusts of wind suggested later drifting.

"It's nice when boys do things for their Pa," commented Mrs. Howe as Al, after hitching Prince, came toward the house rubbing his hands. We watched while the cutter disappeared around the bend.

"It works both ways," said Mother. "Our young people act balky at times like everybody's. But as long as love is strong enough for stretching, and doesn't get discouraged, things usually turn out all right."

11

I thought about what Mother said as I went to school. I could see a long elastic being held by two members of our family, each travelling in different directions. The elastic was thick and wide like that which Mother used to mend the straps of my father's overalls. It might wear very thin, but I had never known it to break.

As I came home again over Naismith's hill, the risen wind strove to drive me back with breath-taking gusts. I sank my chin below my woollen scarf and hurried because we had company and because I was still on the search for romance in Mrs. Howe.

Mother was baking biscuits but she stopped to make me a cup of cocoa and to brew a pot of tea for Mrs. Howe and herself. My sisters were too busy to pause for their share; they were packing and decorating fancy boxes for the Box Social which was to be held in the school-house that night. Some day I would be old enough to go to Socials too but right now my entertainment was the examination of Mrs. Howe. She looked brighter than she had looked when I left for school in the morning and a little happier. Her lips smiled slightly. She had been pretty once. Maybe she had been romantic, too.

"We're in for a heavy storm," the hired men said when they came into the house from the barns for supper. The lamps were already lit. The cretonne drapes were pulled and protected us from window draughts. I couldn't see the storm, but I could hear it. The wind was wailing around the eaves and whistling eerily in the long stovepipe that crossed the kitchen before it entered the chimney in the east wall.

"There won't be many young people at the Social, I'm thinking," prophesied Mother.

But my sisters laughed. "Who's afraid of a little wind and snow?" they asked. With my brothers and our men, they set off in the light sleigh about seven-thirty.

In the old house on that stormy night, there remained only our guest, my mother and me.

𝕒[The Wind That Wasn't Ill]𝕓

While the wind roared furiously in the chimney and snapping
fingers of the frost were heard in the walls of the old house,
sleighs and cutters chimed by, indifferent to the storm.

"They'll have a crowded schoolhouse tonight, in spite of
the bad weather," Mother observed. "It takes more than
snowdrifts and cold to keep young people at home when
there's good fun in store. I'm a bit worried about Mr. Howe
and Frank, though; Puslinch is all hills and hollows and
winding narrow roads. I expect they'll be late for they can't
hurry the horse on a night like this. If it's very bad, they may
stop at Hespeler to give Prince a feed and a rest and to have
a bite themselves. I filled a canvas bag of hot grain for their
feet, going. Coming home won't be so comfortable."

Mother and Mrs. Howe were sitting beside the coal
heater in the living-room. I was bent over my homework at
the table behind them. Mother was knitting a pair of socks.
Mrs. Howe watched her intently as she deftly turned a heel.

"I can't knit."

Mother looked up in amazement. "However do you
manage to keep them all in socks and stockings? The bought
ones don't last long and they're so rough on the skin if
heavy."

"I have a sister who never married. She likes needle-
work and knitting. I always hated it. She used to be a school
teacher; now she's retired and hasn't much to do. It keeps
her busy."

"And I suppose she's fond of your family and interested
in them, having none of her own and being used to children
around her."

"She won't come near us. She doesn't get on with Pa."

"What a pity."

"We haven't room for company that stays all night. The

14

beds are full all the time. When everybody was home, the kids had to double up and there was lots of squabbling over that."

"None of mine ever had a room to themselves, except my youngest. There were two boys and two girls which made it quite simple to plan with the older ones. When Jessie came along, they were half-grown up and didn't want to be bothered with a baby. But now she has a single bed in the girls' room and they make a great fuss over her."

The wind hurled a pail down the veranda steps and Mother opened the door to rescue it, but the storm forced her back inside without it, and a whirl of snow after her.

"It's a really wild night, Mrs. Howe, and getting colder. It's almost time they were home. I hope your husband is warmly clad."

"Orison's always shivering. No amount of clothes keeps him warm."

"He's very thin – he may be anaemic. Thin people feel the cold more than those with a good covering over their bones. Frank used to complain of being chilly a lot, especially when the temperature dropped suddenly and he had to go out in the wind, but now that he weighs more, he never mentions it, although he did buy himself a fur coat for driving, recently."

"That would cost him a pretty penny."

"He needed it long ago but he wouldn't get one until he could afford one for me, too, although really, I don't require it because I go out so little in winter."

"Some get things they can't afford and some can afford things they don't get."

Even to me, this remark of Mrs. Howe's seemed a fairly well accepted fact. I raised my eyes from my homework to look at her with some disappointment and a little disgust. I did wish she would say something to stir the imagination and show some signs of the wayward romantic she was supposed to have been. I had not long to wait.

15

"That's true," from Mother, politely.

From Mrs. Howe, with a nod in my direction, "How old is *she*?"

"Nine, this past October."

"How many years between her and Lily?" Lill was my older sister.

"Almost eleven. It was quite a surprise."

"I never missed more than two years – and twins, twice. My last pair are ten. Ten years and I thought I was finished. I'm not. *And I don't want it.*"

Mother looked sharply at me. She jumped up and snapped shut a damper in the stove.

I stared at Mrs. Howe as if at an apparition.

Smoke from the over-checked fire filled the room. Mother uttered an exclamation and opened the damper a little; then she said in the middle of a cough, "This . . . this . . . is . . . terrible."

But Mrs. Howe and I did not have our minds on the smoke, nor on the wind that was shrieking vengeance in the chimney. Looking straight before her with a stony expression, "And I don't want it," repeated Mrs. Howe.

"My, my, I wish our men were home," Mother said in a loud, nervous voice, picking up her knitting and beginning to join heel and toe with intense concentration. "With a wind like this, anything could happen and as you can see, I can't check the fire much more without it smoking us out, and frame houses don't shed the sparks if they happen to fly out with the smoke."

Mrs. Howe accepted the change of subject politely. "This is a nice house," she observed. "It will be a pity if it burns down."

Her choice of mood brought Mother to a firm pose. "If that happened with Frank away, I'd never forgive myself. It would surely be my fault. He's always so careful and keeps the chimneys clean and the pipes in good shape – no chinks between the bricks nor rusty lengths ever escape his eye.

16

He goes over everything before we light the stoves in the fall. We've lived here so long that the place is a part of us. Of course, it's natural for a family to feel that way about the house they've been brought up in, even if it's old."

Mrs. Howe settled herself firmly against the back of her chair. "Our pipes are dirty," she said statically, "and our chimney has a hole in it as big as your fist."

"But, Mrs. Howe, that's dangerous."

"Yes – very dangerous."

"It's really being pound foolish and penny wise."

"Yes, it really is."

Mrs. Howe spoke without emotion. She cleared her throat and continued, "As I said, just now, I never missed more than two years and. . . ."

Mother interrupted. "Jessie, run to the kitchen, will you, dear, and look down the road? It's past time for your father to be coming."

Unwillingly I went. The windows were thick with frost and driven snow. I lifted the white curtain and blew on the glass until a dark peephole appeared. Now I could see a dark blot on the road that moved up and down like a horse rearing in the shafts. But it was only a sapling straining to resist the wind, and above it the clouds suddenly broke to reveal a slight curve of the moon. As they mended the break, the road, the fields and the hill all became a blur of white again.

I was about to drop the curtain and to return to Mother when a strange dark orange glow to the right against the horizon caught my eye. From it, ruddy tongues that came and went like lightning darted upward. But they were not lightning. The colour was different. *I knew what they were.*

Clearly I could see the dirty pipes and the chimney with a hole as big as your fist.

I ran to Mrs. Howe.

"Your house is on fire," I gasped. "Over there – look."

Mother caught me by the arm. "Jessie – stop it," she said.

Her voice was both frightened and angry but in a matter of seconds she and Mrs. Howe were standing where I had been standing. They were looking to the right as I had looked. I pressed between them. The orange stain was bigger now – it was wider and higher.

Mother didn't bother about me. She threw an arm around Mrs. Howe, whose voice, charged with mingled horror and jubilance, filled the room.

"Our house is on fire," she said. "Our house is on fire!"

Mother gave her a little shake. "Don't think it . . . the child's fanciful . . . there's nothing sure. Roseville is over there . . . a village . . . it might be a dozen places. . . ."

"He wouldn't clean the pipes," went on Mrs. Howe. "He wouldn't mend the chimney. I warned him it would happen. Let it go . . . the whole of it . . . it's not worth saving."

Then she screamed, "The children . . . they're alone." She dropped to her knees. "Lord, don't let it happen to them," she cried. "I told You I didn't want so many . . . I'm sorry . . . don't punish me." She got up and clung to Mother who had bent to me for I was crying from shame at what I had done, and from fright.

"I don't know what to do . . . what can I do? Tell me, what can I do? I must go."

Mother turned to Mrs. Howe with tears on her cheeks. "But it may not be your house at all, we only have suspicions."

Mrs. Howe was putting on her coat.

"I have to go," she said, "my children . . . I have to go. Help me to hitch the horse."

"Of course," Mother said, "I'll do what I can but I can't go with you. The road is in terrible shape and the wind is drifting the snow, but I can't go with you. There's my own house and child to look after."

Mrs. Howe said nothing.

"Bring the lantern from the shed, Jessie," Mother directed, "and put on your things." She caught up a heavy

18

smock of my father's and a thick woollen scarf. I ran at her bidding and while she lit the lantern, I pulled on leggings and rubbers. She bundled me into coat and bonnet and we joined Mrs. Howe at the front door.

The wind stopped us at the foot of the veranda steps. When we could breathe, we went forward, arms raised to protect our faces from the biting blast.

As we reached the stable door, Mother handed the lantern to me. "Hold it steady, child," she said, "and don't come a step nearer."

She led Mrs. Howe into the half-lit stable. I couldn't see them, now, but I could hear Mother speaking to Tom and Bill as she passed them to reach what we called the Visitor's Stall. The lighted lantern fluttered in the wind but I could hear Mother's voice and I wasn't afraid.

I heard Mrs. Howe call, "Daisy", and I heard their mare whinny in reply. I heard the rattle of harness and presently the thumping of hooves as she was backed from the stall. Mrs. Howe led the mare into the yard with Mother following. Mother took the lantern and my hand and held the light where Mrs. Howe could see to hitch Daisy to the cutter. When she had fastened the last strap she leaped into the vehicle and shouted "Giddap", then looked back at Mother.

"Go to your own house and look after it," she called shrilly. "And tell him when he comes, it's the Lord's vengeance."

The mare plunged into the whirling roadway.

For a minute we stood watching but the fierce wind with its white clouds of lifted snow took our breath and we had to turn our backs. We waded through the snow back to the house, and as Mother reached for the door-knob, we heard the chiming of bells, the faint but hopeful sound, which promised everything to us.

"Your father," Mother sobbed. "Jessie, they're coming."

We went back through the snow-filled path to meet them.

They came swiftly; the flame on the horizon was plain,

19

now. Orison Howe leaned forward with a terse question on his lips, "She's gone?"

"Yes, a moment ago. I couldn't prevent her."

My father was already changing the direction of the horse, turning it again to the road. "Go inside and keep warm," he called to us, "I'll be home as soon as I can."

The Howes' house burned down that night, but the children were all safe. When my father and Mr. Howe arrived, only smouldering ruins remained – blackened timbers and twisted iron – children's beds that had withstood the flames. The neighbours had come by field and road and had done their best. They rested with emptied water pails, watching the crumbling embers. Barns and stables had been saved, which was wonderful considering the direction and velocity of the wind. Some men were still on the roof-tops which they had covered with soaked blankets, rescued before the flames had cut off all avenues of entrance to the house.

Mrs. Howe stood with her children around her under a straining pine tree. The older twins, Tommy and Jean, clung to each other, the younger pair leaned against their mother. Rose and Laurie, fifteen and seventeen, stood apart together. Rose was the only member of the family who was crying. She and Laurie had taken their places in the bucket brigade which had brought water from the supply in the barn. The pump by the back door of the house was found to be frozen.

When Orison Howe got from the cutter, my father said, he fell headlong into the snowdrifts in his haste to get to his family, but no one came to meet him. Without moving or speaking, they watched him struggle to his feet alone.

"The man had been neglectful and done wrong, no doubt," said my father, "but there was something inhuman in the way the woman turned on him. 'Well, it's gone,' she said, almost as if it pleased her. 'And the children didn't do it and the storm didn't do it. You did it. You'll have to build a decent house for us, now. We can't live in the barn.'

"He was trembling like a leaf beside me in the cutter all

20

the way. He said over and over that he was to blame. It wasn't easy for him to admit it to me but he did, without offering a single excuse. Now he stood beside his wife and children and listened to her words in a helpless, pitiful state that cut me to the heart. She kept on talking, as if she had never had a chance before and couldn't stop. She said things I'd just as soon forget. 'We're glad it's gone,' she said. 'We're all glad!' She turned to their children and asked them, 'Why don't you tell him? You've told me.'

"He'd had more than enough. I felt like an eavesdropper, hearing what she said, and yet she knew very well that plenty of us could hear. She didn't care.

"I was beginning to feel that there was no hope for the man, when Rose, the tears still on her cheeks, stepped close to him. She put a hand on his arm and said the four words that saved him. 'Pa,' she asked him, 'are you cold?' He broke down and cried like a child."

Things do not always work out the way we want them to but the affairs of the house of Howe did. Mother explained that Mrs. Howe, because of her condition and the shock of the fire, was not herself that night.

In spite of what she said, when Orison Howe built a new house, he built it for thirteen children. The one who was born on Good Friday was a girl and Mrs. Howe named her Orisanna. The story of the fire got into the newspaper in the town where Ronnie was working. He read of it and came home to stay. The new house had a front door, two gothics and a lovely wide veranda.

It did not look the least bit like a mill.

CHAPTER
4

Jimmie Was a Friend

When the days shortened and dusk brought us in early to enjoy the warmth of the old house, my father began to talk about Jimmie Dree and to wonder when he would arrive for his yearly visit.

Jimmie lived a good two miles away but he owned a strip of land and a cottage in our concession. The cottage, built of logs, was never inhabited in my time, except by tramps and fugitives, but the land was low-lying and bore a heavy crop of timothy which Jimmie didn't bother to harvest but had used as pasture for his cows, until a near neighbour with four children was widowed, then he loaned the pasture to her.

Jimmie Dree wasn't a rich man. He had known days of great poverty but his heart, my father said, was as big as a house. He gave with a free hand and seemed to gain by it. He was ten years younger than my father but they were fast friends.

With the first fall of snow, we always listened for the sound of Jimmie's sleigh bells. He usually arrived at nightfall, prepared to stay until morning and to carry my father and my brothers off for a day or two of hunting in the rough lands of Puslinch township. There rabbits, foxes and an occasional bear roamed in the partly cleared sections, or hid in the density of a big swamp. In the past, men had often lost their way in this swamp and one or two had died before help had reached them.

Jimmie was small in stature, hairy and dark. He looked like a Latin but spoke with an Irish brogue and sang Irish airs in a beautiful tenor voice. His parents had been farming folk in the County of Monaghan. His mother, he claimed, had been born in Glasgow but brought up by an aunt in Belfast.

They came to Canada when Jimmie was four years old and settled on the farm which he now owned. He was an only child and when his parents died of typhoid fever contracted from a polluted well, Jimmie inherited the land which he continued to cultivate, working also at a nearby grist as a mill-hand. He was thrifty, as well as generous, and had done well.

His wife was the step-child of one of Jimmie's uncles. She came to Canada when Jimmie was twenty and stayed with the Drees while she worked in a knitting mill in Galt. When Jimmie and she were married, many shook their heads, believing that the pair were cousins and subsequently, when the children arrived, blamed Minnie Dree's hare-lip and Henry's club-foot on this relationship which didn't actually exist. There were four other children, all mentally and physically normal.

I never saw Minnie nor Henry. They had married and moved away from home before I was born. But fragments of gossip about them kept me in constant hope that some day I would see them. It would be something I thought, to look upon a lip made entirely of hair and a foot the shape of a club.

Rabbits were plentiful in those days. "There is no better time for rabbit-hunting than the day after a fresh fall of snow," my father often said, and this was when Jimmie might be expected.

The night before hunting our men cleaned and tested the guns. During this operation, I was banished from the kitchen in case of accident. My time would come when the hunt was over and the hunters settled by the fire for a night of story-telling. All seemed to have had exciting experiences and better luck on previous occasions, but tired and contented they laid plans for a next time.

Jimmie kept several hunting dogs. Two of these were beagles with great melancholy eyes and long silky ears – Bowser and Floss. Bowser was an unfriendly dog who lay alone on a mat which Mother placed behind the stove for him; but Floss took her cue from our collie, Teve, who liked to stretch himself by my father's feet. Floss curled herself before Jimmie, her nose on the toe of his big boot. Now and then, she lifted her head to lean it against his leg, now and then his hand went down to pat her silky neck.

On one occasion, Jimmie lost Floss in the great swamp. For two days, my father and my brothers joined him in a search for her while hunting was forgotten. They came home saddened by her loss, for she was a beautiful, clever creature. There were no rabbits to skin, that night, and Jimmie drove away without the usual rendezvous by the fire.

What was our surprise, the next morning, to hear the sound of his bells, jingling merrily as his horses took the hill! He had come to tell us the wonderful news, part of which we knew before he spoke to us, for Floss rode with him.

The wise creature had found her way home after losing her master in the bush – a distance in all of nearly twenty-eight miles – reaching Jimmie's house at midnight. Mrs. Dree had cautiously answered a sturdy scratching at the door, and Floss had all but tumbled in, to lie down just inside. In two minutes she was fast asleep.

When Jimmie's sleigh turned into his own lane, Floss had leaped up barking happily. Mrs. Dree opened the door for her and she was off like a streak of lightning. She jumped right into Jimmie's lap. It was a wonderful moment for both of them.

My father loved animals and there came a time when he would not kill for pleasure. But when I was a child, he buckled on his heavy leggings and donned his short sheepskin jacket with keen enjoyment. My brothers shared the back of the sleigh with Jimmie's beagles. My father sat with Jimmie on a spring seat across the front. Away they went, bells jingling, into the soft darkness of early morning, to return happy, whatever the kill, for the enjoyment was as much in the outing as in the hunt.

My uncle Alex lived on a farm in Puslinch township and

25

they usually spent the night with him coming home in time for supper the following day. That meal was planned to satisfy the hunger of healthy appetites and to warm the body – homemade broth, enriched by whole beans and diced potatoes, a heaping platter of cold meat with more potatoes, fried, and a dessert of hot suet pudding.

Jimmie always sat hunched on his chair, his head well over his plate. Mother frowned to suppress my sisters' giggles, as each spoonful of soup was drawn in with audible pleasure. Jimmie had little to say until his hunger was satisfied. After a second helping of pudding, he would sit erect, fold his arms and smile into Mother's eyes.

"You've the touch with puddings, Mrs. Beattie," he would say. "There's a special touch to making them, you know. Without it they've the taste of greasy flour."

"Thanks, Jimmie. Have a bit more?"

"Couldn't hold it, lady. Couldn't hold it. Give some to your good man there. He's walked a few miles today."

My father would be yawning behind his hand. Mother shook her head. "One helping's enough for him. He wouldn't be so tired if he didn't have extra pounds to carry. But would you like a spoonful, Frank?"

"No, thanks. I've had plenty, but it was fine and tasty."

There was one visit of Jimmie's which I had occasion to remember.

It had been a perfect summer as to weather, with plentiful sunny days and suitable spacing of showery ones. The vegetables and fruit in garden and orchard had approached record excellence, while in the fields, the grain lifted proud stalks and waved well-filled heads, wheat turning to rich gold, oats to a softer hue, and barley like yellow-tinted white foam.

A row of Montmorencies lined the grey snake fence between a field of clover and the orchard. There was deep dark red fruit in abundance – in such abundance that what the birds claimed was not missed.

I, approaching ten, was pressed into cherry pitting,

26

Mother always added a generous handful of unpitted fruit to every kettle "to lend flavour." She canned and preserved with happy industry, and I watched with delight as the number of jars for winter desserts increased. Cherries were my favourite fruit, cooked or raw. That the jars were inverted troubled me a little until Mother explained that such a method improved the sealing.

Our orchard narrowed toward the west. Two umbrella-like Niagara plums stood on guard just inside the gate. They had a wealth of dark green foliage. They were the "eating" kind, my father said, giving me permission to help myself to as many as I wanted. Unfortunately the two plum trees rarely cooperated, and looking up through the thickly leaved boughs, it was unusual to discover more than one or two orange-red balls per tree. But the flavour was one to be remembered – a tart sweetness, held inside a frail skin which, when punctured, oozed a juice crystal clear and delicate.

There were three rows of apple trees, with Yellow Transparents and Red Astrakans growing nearest the house, the first to ripen, followed by Greenings, Maiden's Blush, Tolman Sweets, Bumburgers, Wine Saps and Russets, with three Northern Spies at the back. Beyond them, filling the V where the snake fences joined, was my favourite tree.

In appearance it was shaped more like a Lombardy poplar than an apple tree – tall, with up-reaching boughs, slim and leafed almost to the trunk. Only the topmost bough, the very point of the tree, was capable of bearing. My father explained that he had done a variety of grafts and although all had "taken", none had yielded fruit. The original species was yellow with pink cheeks, he didn't know the variety, and the fruit appearing as it did at the very tip of the tree, was of little use to anyone, finally dropping into the tall grass below after the first frost.

But each year, I waited for those strange defiant apples to fall, searching the grass for them. They fascinated me. In a way which I cannot explain, I liked their flavour better

27

than that of any other kind in the orchard – strong, bitter, wild, the meat of a hard unyielding texture. Each year I hoped that the taste would alter for the better because a bite or two, a suck of the juice, perhaps, was as much as I could endure for one season. Yet the tree, with its few pink-cheeked non-conformists, was loved by me, and every year I waited hopefully for the autumn frosts when I might find again those globes of blushing gold in the tall grass and test their flavour.

Winter varieties of apples were stored in an over-dark cellar where only trained fingers could identify one kind from another, assisted by the odour rising from the barrel.

"An apple a day, you know," my father used to quote on a winter's night, helping himself from a fruit bowl, always kept well-filled by some one of us.

It was my fondness for apples that caused me to have an uneasy conscience for several months.

A tree of Wealthies stood close to the line fence which separated Jimmie Dree's extra pasture field from one of our own. Each morning and evening from May until October a spindly boy of eight drove the cows to the widow's distant barn for milking but he appeared to take no interest in the apple tree.

"He must be a well-trained boy," Mother said. "I am sure they could well use the fruit. I wonder that Jimmie doesn't offer it to them since he never gathers it himself."

"Why doesn't Mr. Dree pick his Wealthies?" I asked my father.

"Well, I s'pose," he said, "because he doesn't need them. He has a large orchard at home."

"They make good feed for the hungry cows when they fall," Mother commented.

"Too good in my opinion," was all my father said.

Each year the Wealthies grew larger and more plentiful, and I who had much fruit from which to choose in our own orchard became consumed with a desire to taste this luscious kind which belonged to someone else.

The tree leaned away from the fence into Jimmie's field; but the tip of one branch rested on the fence top. It did not bear fruit, however, until I was eleven. That year, when blossoming was ended and the area under the tree white with petals blown off by the wind, there remained two small round green apples in full view.

I watched them ripen. I dreamed of the day when I would see them an alluring gold and red lustre. Perhaps they would tumble into our field and deliver themselves into my yearning hands. Yet I might have known that even if they did, I would not be allowed to lay claim to them.

On my way to school, in a neighbour's yard, stood a spreading strawberry apple tree, and the yard was not fenced. The tree produced bountifully and our neighbour encouraged us to help ourselves to the windfalls. I took one, arriving home with it half-eaten.

"But Mrs. Hilborn told us to take some," I answered Mother's objection.

"That offer was for children without an orchard of their own, not for you," Mother said.

Sometimes, in late autumn when the grassy roadside was strewn with over-ripened specimens, I refrained from breathing as I passed them by.

When my father observed at breakfast one October morning, "The winds are getting stronger. It's time for the Equinox," I listened to him with fluttering heartbeat. Each morning after that day, and each afternoon when I came home from school, I crossed the road from our house to a point where Jimmie's pasture could be seen, until one day the velocity of the wind left no doubt that we had entered the stormy equinoctial period. That evening just as dusk was closing in, the wind became a gale, and with certain footsteps, I went to my usual look-out. The bough leaning over the fence, which had borne two of the finest fruit to be seen anywhere, was flopping limply up and down, as if in mourning.

Deep in the purpling grasses on our side of the fence,

unscarred, I found my twin beauties. I murmured with ecstacy as I lifted one in each hand and made my way to the house.

Mother was waiting for me on the veranda.

"You shouldn't go out in this wind," she said. "You might get hit by something."

I stood, wordless, holding the apples before me, one in each hand, the picture of guilt. "They were in the grass on our side, "I said truthfully, but I am sure that my face expressed self-conviction.

My mother thought a moment. "They are nice, aren't they?" she said, "Put them in the little blue dish on the sideboard. Next time Jimmie comes, we'll give them to him."

Jimmie didn't go rabbit hunting that autumn. The sideboard was in the summer kitchen and almost as cool as the cellar. The apples, in untarnished beauty waited for him.

"Jimmie has a broken toe," my father explained. "He won't hunt this year."

It was February before Jimmie Dree drove up our hill, Bowser and Floss on the seat beside him. Snow was piled high on either side of the roadway. It had been a snowy winter.

His bells drew us to the window. He saw us there and waved merrily. "It's nice to see him again," Mother said.

But I said nothing.

The apples had long ago disappeared from the blue dish. Who removed them I do not know, but I found them, one day, snugly placed side by side in an empty drawer of the cupboard in the summer kitchen which we used for odds and ends.

Occasionally I went to have a look at them. I did so now. They had not rotted but they had withered. The once glossy moons were half-size and cocoa brown, sad evidences of my dishonest intent, and of parental discipline of a nature never to be forgotten.

It was too cold to remain in the summer kitchen or I might have done so, regretfully missing Jimmie's flow of stories, but escaping the humiliation which I believed waited for me. The windows were frost covered and snow had blown through chinks under the door and cracks beneath the loose sash.

After a few minutes of reflection, I closed the drawer with the apples still there. Probably everyone but myself had forgotten about them.

Back in the warmth of the house proper, I sat down on the edge of the wood box. Jimmie nodded and smiled. My father had joined him by the fire and already the kettle was singing while Mother set out scones, home-churned butter and black current jam for them. I was hungry but when I thought of eating there was a lump in my throat.

I noted that Jimmie's beard had grown into a veritable bush and that his hair lay on his neck in crisp curliness. He hadn't had it cut for months he told us. His wife had had a whack at it but the scissors were dull and she had "near pulled the hair out by the roots."

Jimmie's brown eyes were bright with half amusement, half chagrin. He smiled at me as he spoke. Then he turned to Mother.

"Your lass is growing up, Mrs. Beattie," he observed. "When that happens to the youngest, it's always a surprise, isn't it?" Now he turned to my father. "And I think, Frank, this one's going to be the flower o' the family."

My face flamed with shame, not with pride. I got up and returned to the outer kitchen.

As I offered the apples to Jimmie, I said in a sad voice, "The Equinox shook them into our field. I found them in the grass. I'm sorry they dried up."

Jimmie took the small wrinkled things from me, his eyes studying my face. Mother was well-known for her strictness. Jimmie turned to study her face, too, and I was sure that a knowing look passed between them.

"Thank you, lass . . . thank you," Jimmie said in the gentlest voice with which I had ever heard him speak. "The wife has been lambasting me for years to do something with that tree – bring home a graft, you know. But I've been too busy to bother. Did you notice what's happened to it, Frank? The storm got it last week, and 'Serves you right,' she said, 'Now it's a-goner.' But I'll fool her. I'll plant these apples in a sunny corner of the orchard and put some stakes up so nobody will disturb the ground. You've done me a real kindness for sure, Jessie." He turned to me again. "Thankee, thankee . . . the seeds will be black as the pots, come spring, and mebbe they'll give us fruit sooner than a graft would have done."

He slipped the dried things into the pocket of his jacket and smiled again at my father. "Yes, Frank," he said heartily, "she'll be the flower of the family."

I loved Jimmy Dree.

CHAPTER

5

When dark smoke curled from the chimney of our green-houses and the January thaw began, my father placed an advertisement for farm and garden help in the *Globe*. From the replies he selected our men for the oncoming busy season.

"How can you tell from a letter what kind of workman you are getting?" a neighbour asked.

"I can tell," he said.

This was true only in part. Asked to state age and experience, many lied on the second point. For immigrants to Canada at that time, especially from the British Isles, were more often than not from crowded cities, pitifully willing to suffer indignation and scorn when their deception and ignorance of farm practices became known to their employers.

"Why didn't you come right out with the truth?" my father would ask when a man claiming to be an experienced farmer revealed that he couldn't harness a horse.

And more often than not, the low-spoken answer would be, "I was afraid you wouldn't hire me, sir, and I was down to my last shilling."

Among the applications which my father received one year was a well-worded, well-written appeal on expensive stationery embossed with the writer's name – FREDERICK ROGER WILLIAMS – and an address in Toronto's expensive Rosedale district.

My father mused over that letter. He was puzzled. "The way he puts his words together doesn't sound English, Irish or Scotch," he said. "It sounds pretty high-up Canadian to me. Of course he might be staying with a distant relative who could have written the letter for him, but the name wouldn't likely be the same. Paper like that costs a penny, too. There's something queer somewhere. I think I'll give Mr. Williams a chance if only out of curiosity."

Our old house, its logs well hidden under clapboard, sadly needing a coat of paint, had a large living-room into which the front door opened. The Room, as we called it, extended across the full width of the house. An ell-shaped portion led toward the kitchen. When our men amounted to almost a dozen, during seeding-time and harvest, the ell was used as a dining-room. The long drop-leaved table of old walnut had come from my father's home and was big enough to seat twelve comfortably.

My Saturday morning job was to tidy and dust The Room after my sister Lill, eleven years older than myself, had performed the heavier cleaning.

Lill was all bone and sinew, tall, but with a good figure rounded in the right places, and she knew how to accent her charm without immodesty. Lill's wealth of auburn hair was coiled in a figure-eight and her large, slightly mocking blue eyes, her very fair skin, her full ready-to-laugh lips caught the attention of all. I often marvelled at the way in which Lill held herself aloof, tempting but dignified.

Her movements were quick and efficient. Saturday was downstairs scrubbing day for her. The stained and varnished softwood floor of The Room was washed with hot water and homemade soap, no corners missed; the kitchen was scrubbed with a brush, and after the kitchen, in good weather, the unpainted floor of a veranda which ran around two sides of the old house, including a "stoop" where the men paused on the way in to clean their boots with a scraper.

In winter, the veranda was merely swept clean of snow, but it was now the middle of March and unseasonably warm so that Lill gave the narrow old boards their first scrub of the season. By noon, she would appear in a fresh calico dress, probably of lilac, which was her favourite colour, and go swinging down the path to the milk house where additional supplies of food were kept. There were no flowers, yet, but when pansies bloomed, she would stoop lightly, pick one, tuck it into the buttonhole of her dress, singing as she went.

35

I envied Lill her vigour and her light-heartedness. I was as yet an undeveloped child, serious and sickly.

Dusting and tidying The Room was not a brief task. How I hated dusting the many rungs of the cane-bottomed chairs around the table, and the window-sills with their potted plants, geranium, begonia, tear-drop and fern, and a blossoming fuchsia which required careful handling, for it was Mother's favourite houseplant. Mine was a Martha Washington geranium.

It would soon be time to bring out the four-tiered flower-stand from the woodshed to the corner of the house where the veranda turned. It was fashioned so that half of it faced each way and received a fresh coat of green paint every year. Dusting the window-sills would not be so tiresome when the plants were removed.

"Don't forget the upper sash," Mother would call, and I would answer, "No, Mother," while I balanced on a stool to reach the narrow ledges made by the joining of upper and lower. There were no locks in those days. If in fear of marauders, one had only to drive a heavy nail half way into the wood above the join, and even this was seldom considered necessary.

Lill had completed her work that March morning, and with Mother and Jean was busy helping to prepare dinner in the kitchen. I had finished my dusting and was about to relax in my father's arm-chair with a book when someone knocked on the front door.

I opened it. There stood a slender youth holding a fedora hat in his hand, while the wind tossed a mop of blonde hair into very blue eyes. He was stylishly dressed and by the condition of his shoes and trouser legs had obviously walked a long distance through the slush of early spring without either rubbers or heavy boots. His overcoat was light weight fine cloth and the scarf around his neck was paisley silk, not home-knit wool like my father and brothers wore. It was a raw day and he was shivering.

He drew off a kid glove and offered me his hand. My

father's hands were well padded with flesh and always warm, even in the coldest days of winter, and they had hard rough patches as most farmers hands have. How different this hand – so thin and soft and hardly grasping mine at all – taken away almost as soon as offered.

"How do you do?" The young man spoke in a rather nervous voice. "I'm Freddie, from Toronto."

It was by such a name that Frederick Roger Williams became one of our men. But never really one of them, for they rejected him at sight even though my father asked them to be tolerant of this misfit who had come at his request and must be given a chance.

"Little by little, I'm learning why he's like he is," my father said. "The son of a rich man who turns out to be different in nearly every way is always in for trouble. The father's big and husky – Freddie carries around a picture of him in his wallet – he owns a factory and takes for granted that his sons would want to work for him and eventually take over the business. The older boy is making a go of it, but Freddie . . . well, you can see for yourself. He hasn't got it in him to manage anything yet – not even himself. A sad situation. He's made for a different life but nobody will admit it – the mother sides with the father. So, at twenty-one, he's started out on his own, and from what I've learned, they acted glad to get rid of him. It must have taken some guts to leave home just the same, I don't think he ever dirtied his hands before he came here. You should have seen his expression when I set him to mix manure for the hot beds."

"The boy's to be pitied," Mother said.

"Not exactly," my father replied. "He's got a good head on him, if only he'd settle down to respect himself and be himself. But he has no self confidence and he'd give anything to be somebody else. I heard him using words yesterday that Old William uses when he's getting over a spree and they didn't belong to Freddie.

Old William, too, was a misfit. He was quiet when sober,

but showed a vicious temper and a coarse tongue after a weekend in town. He boarded in the village but had dinner with the rest of our men, never showing his real self no matter what the provocation, when in the house. This was a disappointment to me. I felt that I did not know Old William and he interested me. Good people were not half so interesting as those who were considered wicked.

Old William was short and slight, and a little bent. His hair was graying. He had small unrevealing eyes and very thin lips. He rarely shaved. When he did, I was always astonished to note that he resembled the King of England, but not even my father, the confidant of so many, knew Old William's past.

Freddie had been with us two months now. My father used him as light garden help and he worked faithfully enough, but without ambition. My father praised him when he honestly could, he told us, but admitted that he wasn't making any headway with this strange, silent boy. "He almost never talks. He does laugh when the other men do, but you feel that he doesn't know what he's laughing at. His mind isn't with them." I could see that my father worried about Freddie. Our men had their special places at the table which they resumed each day. It was not without forethought that Freddie was given the chair beside my father.

Waiting with Mother and my sisters in the kitchen for the "second" table one evening I could hear the men talking and laughing in The Room. When the supply of food needed replenishing, it was always Mother who brought the dishes to the kitchen to be refilled. She had her reasons, no doubt, my sisters were comely girls.

The Room was a friendly place at all times and in spring the sun, as it went down, flooded golden through the west window and threw a scarf of light across the table. Spring was slow in coming that year and late frosts were threatening the early blossoms. But its approach cheered everyone, for the winter had been long and snowy. It was suppertime and as usual I sat in the kitchen, listening to the merriment of the men, for they were very talkative that night, and my father and my brothers with them.

Mother spoke thoughtfully, as she helped Jean to refill a huge bowl with preserved crab apples, "It's good they have some enjoyment," she said, "Most of them have nobody or are too far away to get to them very often."

"Freddie has somebody," I protested, "A whole family. He showed me their picture, but he doesn't laugh like the others do."

"Freddie has nobody," Mother said.

I was about to answer when the voice of Old William held our attention. He was telling how a young policeman in town the night before (where William had been indulging his taste for alcoholic beverages) had endeavoured to eject an unruly customer from the general store. In doing so he had tripped over a full basket of eggs, carrying the whole basket out into the street on his boot, to the shouted laughter of the onlookers.

Our men found the incident and Old William's way of telling it just as funny but as he ended his story and the merriment of our men lessened, I realized that Freddie had not laughed with them. I was sitting on a stool by the kitchen table in direct line with where my father sat in The Room. I could see Freddie distinctly and he was not even smiling. Instead there was a look of great unhappiness about him, he had given the impression of listening with the others, but he had not heard a word. He was in some secret world of his own. Yet the longing to be one of them was a dark shadow on his face. Suddenly, like a high soprano in a choral, his voice followed the laughter.

"And I always dip my cookies in my tea."

Cookies! Why cookies? They had not been included in the evening meal.

Jean set down the jar of fruit which she was holding. Mother stopped with spoon suspended. Lill and I looked at each other in stunned silence. There was silence in The Room, now, too, broken only by the scraping of chairs as the men rose from the table. Finally no one was left there but my father and Freddie. I saw Freddie looking nervously around the empty room and at my father, whose eyes avoided meeting his.

Then The Room was deserted and the house was very still. Still except for the muffled laughter of Lill who had collapsed on a chair in the kitchen, with her hands over her mouth.

I did not laugh because I was not amused. I had the feeling that someone had laughed in church or at a funeral.

Soon Jean was replacing the crab apples in the jar and Mother was starting to clear the table. "Too bad they missed their extra serving of fruit," Jean said quietly.

"They all had good helpings the first round," Mother replied.

Lill was still rocking from side to side on her chair in the corner, when my father came in to the kitchen, but after a look at his face, she struggled to control herself, wiping her eyes with the corner of her apron.

My father looked sternly at her. "This is no laughing matter," he said in a deep voice. "That boy's as sick as if he had a disease of the body. He needs help. I don't know how to give it to him, but he needs it."

When my father's voice deepened like that we all came to attention.

"I'm sorry," Lill said. "But it did sound so – so loony."

"That's just it," my father answered her. "It was loony."

The next day was Saturday. No school and no need to get up early, but Jean woke me with a gentle shake of the shoulder before the sun had risen.

"You'll have to go for the cows, this morning Jessie. Get up, it's almost six o'clock."

"Lill always fetches them. I'm sleepy."

"She can't, this morning. She's busy. I'll tell you about it later, and when you come down, go out by the front door.

Don't go into the kitchen. There's a very special reason why you mustn't, dear."

I sat up. When Jean called me "dear" I was more likely to obey promptly.

"Did you sleep well, last night?" she asked kindly.

"Yes, but I have a toothache. I had it yesterday, too."

"I'll tell Mother; and when you bring the cows, she'll fix you up with a poultice of hot vinegar and pepper."

I winced. I had felt such poultices before, applied with a covering of brown paper, and outside of that, a pad of flannel which one kept warm by pressing it against the stove-pipe now and then.

I jumped out of bed. "I don't need a poultice," I said. "It's getting better."

When I went down the stairs which led into The Room, the door into the kitchen was closed. The table was laid for breakfast. It was not yet six-thirty but the men would be in shortly, for they must be in the fields by seven.

While I had dressed, Jean had asked me, "Did you hear any noises in the night?"

"No. Why?"

"Oh, I just wondered. Nobody walking around or on the stairs?"

"No. Why, Jean?"

"Well, sometimes the men are late going to bed."

"Was somebody late, last night?"

"I don't think so. Now away you go." She buttoned my red cotton pinafore which closed at the back.

The cows were in the southwest pasture and as I went along the road which divided our land almost in half, the sun was tipping above the eastern horizon and flooding the grey flanks of cloud with watermelon pink. Birds were up with the sun, carolling from tree and fence post. I might have dawdled had it not been for something mysterious in Jean's voice when she asked me questions. I threw open the field gate, shouted to the cows and was relieved when they came eagerly. There would be fodder in their troughs, for the grass was still young, and relief for their udders when human hands stroked them.

When I had driven them into the yard beside the barn, I shut the gate and hurried to the house. The men would tie them in their stalls, and later, after breakfast, Mother and my sisters would proceed with the milking.

Jean and Mother were sitting in The Room, sipping tea. The men had eaten and gone out. Standing by the window, Lill, with red eyes, was trying to stop crying.

When I sat down, she left the window and went to the kitchen to get a bowl of porridge for me.

"What's wrong?" I said, as Lill set the bowl before me.

Lill cried some more. "I'll never make fun of anybody again," she wept. "It's the meanest thing I ever did."

I knew then that something had happened to Freddie.

When the men went to bed the night before, Freddie had gone with them. He slept alone in a small room above the kitchen. Mother had given him "the little bedroom" as we called it, at my father's suggestion, because, he said, "The others might pick on him if he shares a double. They haven't any respect for him."

Because Freddie roomed alone and because his first job on arising at five o'clock was to feed and water the setting hens in a shed near the greenhouses, only the hens were aware that he hadn't done so.

While the men went about other chores, Lill had set off in the half-light of a cloudy dawn for the cows. She had gone only a few yards along the road to the southwest pasture, when she saw a figure limping toward her and had recognized Freddie. He had walked all night, he said, (because lying down under a tree, he had found the cold unbearable), and after stumbling along in the darkness over stony roads, in thin shoes, his feet had become so sore and blistered that he had decided to turn back.

Freddie had walked along home with Lill, who had assured him that none of the men would guess that he'd run away. With Mother's help, a bucket of warm suds was filled in the shelter of the woodshed, and while Freddie sat with his feet immersed, Lill brought him a bowl of porridge and remained to speak words of encouragement. Freddie had admitted to her that he thought no one in the world cared anything about him.

When my father opened the woodshed door, Freddie stood up in his bucket and spoke "more like a grown-up," my father said, "than I had ever heard him do."

"I'll never do this again, Mr. Beattie," he promised. "Will you take me back?"

"I'll take you back because you have become a man," my father answered him.

But a few weeks later, Freddie left us.

"It's no use," my father admitted, "Try as I have, it's no use. The others won't have a thing to do with him. He'll never live the cookies-in-the-tea down. I've spoken together and alone with the men. They don't upset him by what they say or do, it's what they don't do, and don't say. Freddie's sharp, he feels their scorn and it's sapping what little confidence he has gained. He needs encouragement and he's not getting it here."

It was June now and the loveliness of nature was everywhere. The scent of flowers and of ripening strawberries was in the air. The fragrance of clover came from coils of drying hay in the warm sun. On the pasture hills and in verdant valleys sheep and cattle roamed, lambs kicking up their heels and bleating their joy.

I was recovering from one of my sick spells, the origin of which the doctors had not yet determined. A couch had been placed for me on the veranda and I could see the men gathered under an elm tree which shaded the grass at the distant side of the lawn. They were talking and one or two were singing, all were seated except Freddie who was roaming around, looking at the flowers, viewing the sky, coming over at last to hand me a verbena which had, he said, been lying broken from its stem. It was pink and sweet smelling. Always when I see verbenas I think of Freddie.

The clatter of wheels announced that someone was coming along the road and up the hill, which I could not see from where I lay. Freddie took a look around the corner of the house. "The well-diggers," he said. "Your father said they were coming, tonight, to dig on the farm up there." He pointed toward the south where McNally's buildings could be distinguished behind a grove of evergreens.

The McNallys had depended for years on a spring for their water supply, but it had failed them now.

Jim and Tom had been digging wells in our district for many years, they were a common sight, travelling around in the spring and summer months, with their queer looking equipment mounted on a wagon built for the purpose.

They stopped at our house now, to have a word with my father.

He stood talking to them with his boot on the hub of the wagon wheel, elbow leaning on his knee. After a brief conversation with them, he came into the house while they waited. Mother was sewing by lamp-light at the living-room table.

"They need a helper," my father said to her. "Not to dig, just to fetch and carry, and other light jobs and they wondered if I might have a hand that I could spare. The fellow they had hired for the season ran a nail into his foot and it's festered. They don't know when he'll be back, maybe not at all. It's a chance for Freddie if he'll take it; he's getting nowhere here. What do you think?"

Mother spoke low but I caught her words. "Is it a safe job?"

"Quite safe, Jim says. Above ground, no pick and shovel work either."

"You could ask him, Frank, but don't let him feel that you want him to go. He's only got us. But if he's that nearby, he can come and visit."

44

"That's what I thought."

Lill was playing the organ in the parlour and she and Jean were practising a song to be rendered at the Christian Endeavour the following week. They had stopped to listen.

"The quicker the better," my father said, "and everybody stay where they are. I don't know how he'll take it."

I lay still on my couch while my father called to Freddie and went into the kitchen with him. I felt a strange melancholy when my father came outside alone.

After a few minutes, I heard footsteps in The Room and then Mother's voice. "So you're going to leave us for a while, Freddie?" Her voice was gentle. "Well, now, that will be a nice change for you, and so close by. We'll miss you but you can come back easy. Maybe next Sunday night for supper?"

There was a moment's silence before an unsteady voice said, "Thank you, Mrs. Beattie."

Freddie waved a cheery hand to me as he passed me by on his way to the waiting wagon. He climbed up on a shaft of the well-digger and stood gaily waving to the men under the tree. Only Old William returned his wave.

Mother came out to watch them drive away, wiping her eyes on the corner of her apron. Later, she said that Freddie had tried to speak his thanks, couldn't, and had kissed her hand.

Freddie became an heroic figure in our community a few months later. While the diggers were eating their lunch, a small child fell into an unfinished pit. Freddie hearing her cry, had jumped in, knowing perfectly well the danger of the partly-built structure caving in. After handing her to someone over the ledge, he had been buried by quantities of crumbling earth and other debris.

When an attempt to dig Freddie out failed because of more cave-in, a pipe was forced down to carry air to him and a shout went up when there was a rapping on the pipe. A second well was dug beside the first in an attempted rescue, although no one thought the boy would live through the ordeal.

The whole neighbourhood gathered around the place, my father with them.

"There's no more sound," Jim said finally. "He's stopped rapping on the pipe. We might as well give up."

My father put his mouth to the pipe-end, using it as a speaking tube. "We're coming, Fred," he shouted. "Don't give up, boy. We're coming." There was a feeble tap on the pipe again, and a cheer went up as the men dug on.

Darkness fell before they had completed their task, and before Freddie from Toronto was hoisted to the surface, where a doctor stood waiting.

Freddie would live, but during his ordeal, his hair had turned snow-white.

When next I saw Freddie, it was 1914. He came to say goodbye to us before leaving for France with the Canadian army, a sturdy looking young man with a fresh ruddy complexion, his eyes confident and happy. He had already won his first stripe and hoped for another, he said.

"All he needed was self-respect," my father declared. "Others took it away from him when he was a child. He had to win it back."

CHAPTER
6

ৡ[Adam, Scientist]৫

When Adam Brown, in his trim red cutter drawn by a team of well-groomed bays, passed through our lane gate one stormy March afternoon, I heard my father say, "Four o'clock. Company for supper, Ma. I'll slip down and help the boys with the chores, Adam will want to see the stock anyway. I guess you've plenty of everything on hand; if not there'll be time to bake. We should have supper early, though, or we won't get to bed until morning. Not likely we will anyway."

Adam could talk a leg off an elephant, my father often said, yet he seemed glad when Adam came, although I had heard him heave a relieved sigh when the man was finished "speaking his mind" and had expressed the intention of going home.

Adam Brown was of good height and strongly built, with bushy red hair, sideburns, and a sweeping moustache. The exposed area of his face was a shiny pink, deepening over the cheek bones and on the round of the chin. His eyes were a clear, steady blue and reflective, Mother said they had a far look in them. His aquiline nose was well-dented at the bridge, his mouth full-lipped and firm.

Adam was an impressive speaker. "Everybody in a meeting listens," my father said, "when Adam Brown gets to his feet."

People who remembered Adam Brown's mother declared that he was very like her. She had come from a carriage-making family in Edinburgh. Her father had been against his daughter marrying a farming man, who intended emigrating to Canada, but love had its way and to Canada the young couple came. Writing home, Eliza Brown had mentioned that the only vehicle in which they had to ride was a four-wheeled wagon.

48

"It must have been very difficult for the girl," Mother explained. "Corduroy roads were still in use in my young days and it was impossible for Eliza to sit erect. But after they received her letter, Eliza's family sent out a handsome carriage all lined with grey plush, with arm supports and a footstool. Eliza could sit erect in that. But when they went to church, Adam's father, a slender dark man, quite shy, used to give her a hand to get down, and then disappear to escape the chuckles of the other farmers, who thought wagons were the proper means of travel in a country such as Canada then was."

The part of the story which I enjoyed hearing most, however, concerned the second wife of Adam's father. For after bearing a son and two daughters, Eliza had caught a cold which had turned into "consumption". She had died after a year of illness.

The second Mrs. Brown was a pert, bossy young lady. "Not really a lady at all," so my father explained. "She had plenty of go to her and was a help in raising the children but although I was only a child at the time, I felt glad that Lucky, as the neighbours called her, was not my mother.

"She was a silly girl, although she soon had children of her own. The saying is that she could use her tongue as smartly as she used a switch. The step-son left home and the step-daughters married as soon as they could, I imagine. Nobody knew much about what happened in the Brown's house after that."

But one story leaked out, he remembered, and it was chuckled over for a long time. It appears that Lucky was very jealous of Eliza. I have no doubt that Adam's father cherished Eliza's memory for she had been a fond wife, Mother said, in spite of her dignity. In contrast, Lucky was shrewd and demanding and the mere mention of Eliza would result in a fit of rage vented upon her husband, who took it mildly, quietly leaving the house for a walk in the fields.

Perhaps his habit of leaving before she had finished

speaking was responsible for an act which turned every other woman in the community against her.

One day, after an argument over the dinner table, Lucky, in a fit of rage and jealousy, picked up the half-full teapot and walked to the carriage house where Eliza's gift from her parents was kept, but no longer used, for Lucky would not ride in it. She opened the carriage house door, undid the door of the carriage, and with perfect aim threw the entire contents of the teapot over the plush upholstery.

"Her disrespect of Eliza was hurtful to a husband who was always a little afraid of her, I think," Mother explained. "He was a man of few mistakes but he made one for certain when he married Lucky, although she had a sweet way with men, as a girl."

"Poor unhappy Brown died the next year," my father said, "and Lucky came into her own, for the farm and almost everything that he had, was left to her. She didn't make good use of her possessions, though. She became a real miser, lived alone in a big house, stopped going to church or anywhere among folks, and ate herself to death, so the doctor said. From a slim girl she became a woman with dropsy so bad that the shape of her body was like an over-stuffed bag."

"That's not nice, Frank," Mother remonstrated.

"It wasn't," he grinned. "But it was true and you know it. Remember the day you were picking blackberries along the road fence and found her stuck between the rails."

Mother stifled a laugh, then. "Poor soul, she was so ashamed. I helped her out and she started off toward home without even a word of thanks. Of course I was only a young thing and I suppose she was too embarrassed to speak."

I was never weary of hearing stories about the Brown family, nor of listening to Adam. I knew what my father meant about the attention Adam commanded from other men, for although I was a child and unable to decipher the full meaning of his profundity, I held a great respect for his views. If I managed to escape Mother's habit of sending me early to bed, then this would be another night to remember.

I drew my small rocking-chair to a half-hidden position between my father's arm chair and the oval table which was centred by a large lamp and littered with papers and books, for my father was a reader. My position was also near our coal heater with the red and purple pictures made by its leaping flames in the bed of coal burning behind the mica. It had been a bitter day and my father pulled on his sheepskin jacket and a heavy cap before going out to meet his friend.

After placing my chair in readiness, I watched from the window. Adam tossed the buffalo robe from his knees and supported himself by holding on to the cutter while he gained a firm footing in the deep snow. He turned, then, and removed a thick mitten before giving his hand to my father in greeting. My father's hand was bare and I smiled with a sense of his superiority over Adam Brown. My father's hands were always warm, even in zero weather, and unknown to mittens. When riding with him on a very cold day, I had only to tuck the two of mine into one of his and I, also, did not require mittens.

I watched him help to unhitch the bays and to lead the way to the stables. The horses would be given a good feed and would rest in the visitors' stall until Adam left for home.

I waited impatiently for the friends to appear. They waded through the freshly-fallen snow to the house.

Adam's manner contained an element of self-esteem, not to be mistaken for conceit. He greeted Mother politely and, in a dignified deliberate way, went about removing his greatcoat and fine fur cap which he hung on a wall peg beside my father's rougher garments. Then he rubbed his hands and blew into them as he approached a chair which Mother had set by the fire for him, welcoming him with, "Come away in, Mr. Brown. You'll be needing a cup of tea after a drive in the cold. The wind is extra sharp." She had placed a kettle on the range and it could be heard sputtering. She hastened to the kitchen to attend to it.

Other friends of my father's might be addressed by their first names but never Adam Brown.

As he settled in the chair, I stood off a little, watching. He turned to smile at me and I attempted to see into his large blue eyes, for something mysterious lay there. While one knew that nothing in his surroundings escaped his observation, his cognizance was casual, as if he had more important matters on his mind. If one were respectful and listened long enough, one might catch a glimpse of what such matters were before he set off home again. What I did not understand only encouraged me to wait for what might be understandable. In an inexplicable way even the presence of Adam Brown was exciting.

I can remember my father's sober quietness after one of Adam's visits. Mother would say, "What are you thinking about?" and he would answer evasively, "Oh, just thinking, Ma."

I was usually sent to bed before the visitor left but I rarely slept until I heard his brass cutter bells jingling off through the wintry darkness. It would be midnight at least, often far after. Visiting was an important part of Adam's life, and his stimulating conversation and original ideas made him different enough from the rest of the farmers to win for him the deference of his neighbours and the title, "Adam, the scientist."

Adam was not much of a reader, my father said. He spent his time turning over and over the mysteries of life and trying to solve them by means of his own capacity for original thought. "But he makes other people do a lot of wondering," my father would add, "and some of them wouldn't think past their noses if it weren't for Adam prodding them into doing it."

He would lean forward on his chair, lay his hands together, finger along finger, and speak without pause or consideration for those listening who might want to express an opinion, too. When finished, he would lapse into reflective silence, not appearing to hear any responses to his dissertations, sitting motionless and with eyes closed as if in communion with some other world. In winter, after a long drive in the cold air followed by contact with the heat of the coal fire in The Room, he would doze, with his shiny pink chin resting comfortably on a light blue home-knit muffler, which he always wore in cold weather.

I would watch eagerly for Adam to wake. When he did so, it was with the expression of one emerging refreshed from an invigorating bath. The blue eyes seemed more blue, the words flowed with more ease and eagerness.

"Yes Frank," he would say, "the great miracle of creation is about to happen. Notice how the cold is increasing year by year? Some don't record anything, but I have kept a chart since I was a boy and that chart tells the truth. Look at something accurate and you can speak with accuracy, pay attention to the little signs and there you will find the big sign. We're about to enjoy a complete change. There'll be ice upon ice and snow upon snow, ice upon ice and snow upon snow, and," he paused, fitted his hands together by threading the fingers, then quickly turned the hands over with a sharp twist of the wrists. "As sudden as that," he went on, "we'll be in the Torrid Zone. It's coming. This is the year of the unexpected, Frank, it's time that we had our share of easy living, we've worked hard, nature is fair and reasonable, the fruits of the land without labour will be ours soon."

Adam was a vegetarian and by his orders, Mrs. Brown and their six sons, also. The sons, Mother often marvelled, were sturdy, tall young men. Meat or a meat substitute in our family was considered a necessary food for health, "But Adam thinks differently," my father explained. "He says the flesh stupid man feeds on is the flesh of creatures who eat nothing but vegetation. Man is then eating fodder when he eats meat but not in the form suitable for his consumption."

53

"Mrs. Brown never seems to ail," Mother observed. "When the boys were born, I envied that woman. The births were so easy. And she had no trouble after."

Adam's pockets were known to be store-houses of butternuts and home-grown walnuts. In the fruit season, when he came to call, he often carried a dish of cherries or plums freshly picked. I had never seen the Brown's orchard but my father said it was a full acre in size with every variety of fruit tree that could be grown in our climate. "I may be imagining things," he said, "but unless my eyes deceive me, Adam's trees bloom bigger and better than any of ours. And the fruit has a special flavour."

Mother agreed.

It was the winter of 1910 and many people were on the watch for the return of Halley's Comet which, it was said, was visible every seventy-five years, an astronomical event of such importance that preachers spoke of it from their pulpits, and teachers to their classes in school. To the people who believed that signs in the sky were associated with the end of the world, the coming of the comet created a fearful ecstasy.

Adam lowered his voice almost to a whisper, while he discussed the phenomenon with my father. "Did you read in the paper that anybody looking for it will be blinded?" he asked. "That, Frank, is a fallacy. It's a fallacy because I have proved it to be; I look for the thing every night and what is more . . . *I have seen it*. Not with a telescope, mind you, with my naked eye. *Look and ye shall see*. Yes, sir. But the eye has to be trained, day by day, and not many bother to train it. I have seen the comet, Frank. It looks like a star with a tail and it is my opinion that it shrinks after becoming full-grown, into a mere spark, and stays that way, out of sight, until the time comes for it to show itself; then it begins to grow. I seem to hear a humming in the sky while I look, as if it is saying something to me. Just born, Frank, but growing fast, and wanting to speak to man."

"They claim it won't be in view for a while yet," my

father objected mildly, but Adam set his heavy lips in a supercilious smile. "I have seen it, Frank," he repeated.

While Adam enjoyed his second doze that night, Mother and my father exchanged a doubting look, but I slipped from my chair to the window which was unshaded. The sky was scattered with stars but where should one search? I hadn't any idea, but remembering that the Christmas star was said to be visible in the East, I looked there for the comet, too.

"Could be, you know. Could be," I heard my father murmur, passing a hand reflectively over his beard. He had respect for Adam's wish to be honest. He, too, pondered a great deal over the mysteries of creation, not arriving at the same conclusions but thinking . . . thinking. . . .

"Time for you to go to bed," Mother warned me in a whisper, noticing me in spite of my attempts to efface myself. "It's after ten . . . nobody can tell how long. . . ." She paused and nodded toward the sleeper, but as if in defence of me, he woke.

"Yes," he resumed, "I have seen the comet, Frank. Men who believe in visions should pay more attention to realities. Those men in their observatories, they depend too much upon their telescopes. What were our eyes made for if not to note the wonders of the world and what some call the heavens? I've surpassed these men, Friend; but I shall not tell them, I am amused by their boastfulness. You read your Bible, I read mine, but we do so for different reasons. You read yours to save you from perdition, I read mine to be saved from ignorance. There's wisdom in that Book, it lays down a design for man's thinking. Take the passage about babes and sucklings." He turned toward me where I sat leaning against my father's knee. "Jessie," he asked respectfully, "Have you seen queer things in the sky, sometimes?"

I nodded. I musn't go against my father, but I *had* seen many queer things – mountains of pearl with deep caves of grey, clouds like horses tossing dust from their feet as they passed through dawn or sunset, twinkling lights that smiled

55

and frowned and were surely more than just mere stars.

"Have you," Adam asked me softly, "seen a star with a tail?"

Halley's Comet had appeared previously and gone, of course, long before I was born, but hearing so much about its return, I had studied the skies, too, and, yes, several times, gazing for a long period I had thought I saw a strong line of light passing from the brightest of stars downward. I was a truth-teller by training.

I got up and went to Adam's side, all the while keeping a hand on my father's knee as if for protection from I knew not what.

"Yes," I admitted, speaking timidly, "There is one with a tail. There really is one."

There was silence in The Room. Adam smiled sweetly at me but Mother and my father looked sober. The most severe rebuke which I had ever received from my father was a sober look. I could not endure it. I moved away from Adam and climbed onto my father's knee, threading my arms around his neck and hiding my face on his shoulder. His arms closed around me and I knew than that he wasn't angry. "I thought I saw a tail, I did think I saw one."

"Of course," he answered me gently. "Maybe **you** did. We don't all see the same things when we look. I'm getting old. My sight isn't what it once was."

I went to bed, then, leaving three silent people. But while I undressed in the bedroom above The Room, I heard Adam begin to talk again. I felt somehow condemned and later I got out of bed for another look at the sky. There were many stars but I couldn't find one with a tail, now. I didn't care. I was more concerned with another matter.

The stove-pipe from the coal heater in The Room passed upward through my bedroom and on into the chimney. The storm was increasing and with it a high wind which wailed mournfully.

Kept awake by the rise and fall of voices below and the

moaning wind, I heard the door open and close. Finally, Adam had started for home and my father, of course, accompanied him to the stable, carrying the lantern and helping him to hitch the bays. I sat up in bed to watch.

When the cutter turned into the road and snow flew upward like smoke as the horses broke their way through the heavy drifts, my father stood looking after his friend. Then, he put a hand up to shade his eyes and looked for a long time into the sky.

When he turned and came toward the house, finally, I lay down and tried to control the tears which had been wetting my pillow. But the sorrowing wind encouraged them. The comet was forgotten. "My sight isn't what it once was," my father had said.

How could I bear it? My father was growing old.

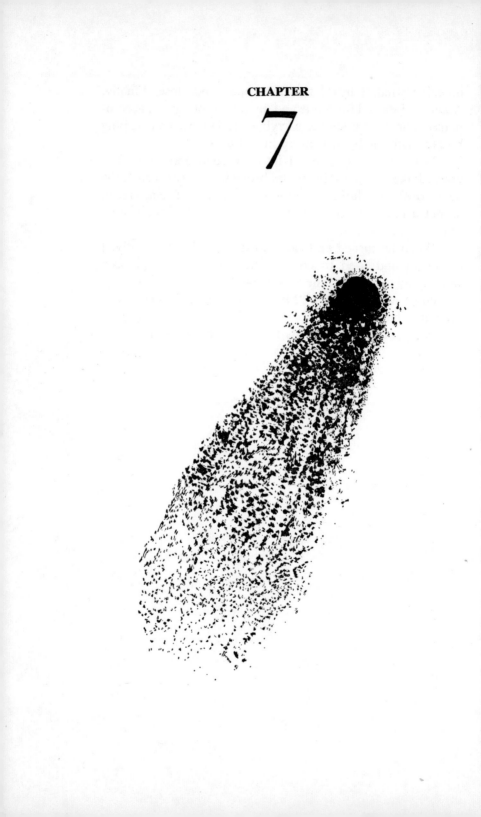

Ezra and the Comet

Among the travelling preachers of our time, searching for souls to save, was Ezra Slade. When he visited our village of less than one hundred inhabitants, conducting his evangelistic services in a small union church, or in an outdoor setting, according to the season, Ezra sought out my father as an unfailing friend.

"If I could speak from that hill, Frank," I have heard him appeal. "It would suit the purpose perfectly."

The hill Ezra coveted overlooked a valley in one of our pastures. It was a fertile valley with a wide stream crossing through; the bank of the stream was lovely with long stemmed violets and low white daisies, in their season; later, with wild purple asters, and delicate buttercups on frail green stems.

Between the hill and the stream was a stretch of smooth meadow grass mingled with clover. Honey bees droned there. The area of the valley was large enough to accommodate the population of the village and many from the countryside around it. "But usually Ezra's lucky," my father said, "if he brings out a few dozen, maybe thirty or forty people. The man has every intention of doing good; he doesn't shout at them, he hasn't the physical strength to shout. He might better speak from a pulpit, but he preaches hell-fire and damnation just the same, and because his voice is mild, they listen."

My father was a Presbyterian and accustomed to dignity even in evangelical efforts. I knew that, while he respected Ezra, he did not approve of his methods or doctrine.

The outdoor preaching in summer often took the form of a small camp-meeting except on rainy days. People began to bring picnic lunches and to stay for two services, thus making of the church attendance a kind of holiday. Ezra, cheered by their show of interest, added some musical talent to his presentation in the form of two singers and a drummer, who arrived daily in a rickety old open buggy. They became quite an attraction.

As a child, I was not allowed to attend Ezra's services and although my father went frequently, and occasionally my brothers and sisters, Mother remained at home with me. Her Presbyterian background dated to five hundred years and she was most offended by lack of dignity in religious worship.

One evening, when sounds from the hill indicated more fervour than usual, Jean who had Mother's dignity, came quietly into the house when the service was scarcely under way.

"What's wrong, Jean?" Mother asked.

Jean was a handsome young woman with dark eyes which could flash fire in times of disapproval, although they were usually lit by a tenderness which characterized her nature. They flashed, now.

"I couldn't take it, Mother," she said. "Milly Ross was there. She claimed to be filled with the Spirit and took a fainting spell after crying out in a horrible manner. She had to be carried off to one side by two of the men and laid on the grass by herself. It wasn't religion, Mother, and I'll never go again."

"Why didn't you bring Lill home with you?"

"Lill?" Jean smiled. "For her it was so funny. I expected her to laugh out loud and she probably would have, if Father hadn't had his eye on her. Will and Al were disgusted, too, I could see."

Ezra arrived summer after summer. Usually he was billeted by one or another of his own sect, of whom there were several in the community; but he came to have a meal with us at least once a week.

Ezra was tall and spare. His skin was sallow and beginning to wrinkle although my father said he wasn't much past forty. His pale brown hair lay thinly over his oval-shaped head in lifeless inadequacy, his large ears stood out on either side of an unusually narrow face with fallen-in cheeks.

"The poor man isn't to blame for his looks," Mother said when my sisters expressed distaste for the visitor at our table. "Whoever took care of him as a baby didn't know enough to flatten his ears before they laid him down."

But Ezra's eyes were his dominant feature. They were very large and distinctly oval with tight lids. They protruded unpleasantly and were absolutely expressionless.

"If he couldn't see with them," my father observed, "you'd say they had no purpose."

"They're like big beads," Mother said.

But for me, Ezra's eyes had a fascination, because they resembled a large brooch which Mother wore on Sundays. It had been sent to her by a grand-aunt in Scotland. I mentioned this likeness to Mother, one day.

"Over there," she said, "the stone is known as a sheep's eye."

"That's it," Lill giggled. "Ezra's eyes are like a sheep's."

"I wish you wouldn't wear it any more, Mother," Jean pleaded. "I hate it."

Lill agreed with her. "Don't wear it, Ma," she urged. "It will remind me of that queer man every time I look at it now. I'll think, 'Ezra's lost an eye,' and whenever I see him, I'll think, 'Ezra's got two brooches like my Mother's, but he wears them in the wrong places.'"

"Girls, girls," from Mother. "As I said before, the poor man can't help his looks."

While he was in the neighbourhood, Ezra took it for granted that he would never be unwelcome at our table. If the day were rainy and he could not hold a service, he might arrive in time for the noonday meal and stay until after supper. He didn't remain in the house, however, but followed my father wherever he went, "although never offering to lend a hand with anything," my father observed rather

61

than complained. At our table Ezra had a ready assembled congregation.

Here, indeed, he must have considered, were souls to be saved. But our men continued to think their own thoughts and talk among themselves, while Ezra attempted to interject purposeful remarks, through a conversation with my father. But my father had respect for more than Ezra. He listened politely when occasion required it of him, but when the trend was toward evangelism, he quietly changed the subject.

Alone with us, my father would say, "If he talks religion and nothing else, the effect will be bad. He needs variety in his own life, too. At noon, he mentioned the importance of fasting, but nobody could deny that he was putting away a hearty plateful at the same time. I noticed grins and nudges."

"They say, though, that fasting helps to clear the mind," Mother observed, "and I suppose it has its place, especially in the lives of people who don't do physical work."

"Maybe; but he's planning on going on a two-week fast, this fall, after the summer preaching is over. I doubt if the man's altogether sensible. He'll probably end up in a hospital."

But the following early spring found Ezra at our door again, looking healthier than I had ever seen him, and his eyes – yes! They now had a kind of happy lustre and an expression of expectancy.

I was playing with my dolls in the kitchen where Mother was baking bread. My sisters were upstairs house-cleaning, but doing more laughing than working, I thought. As Ezra knocked, Lill had just burst into a selection from some opera and Jean had lowered her contralto voice in an attempt to answer as a basso.

"Why, come in, Ezra," Mother greeted him. "The wind is still chilly, isn't it? Hang up your coat behind the stove, there, and sit down. Frank is in the greenhouses. It's transplanting time for the late celery you know. How is the family?" Ezra had a wife and two children whom we had never seen.

"Just fine, just fine, thank you, Mrs. Beattie."

Ezra sat down.

"And yourself?"

"Wonderful. Just wonderful, ma'am."

While Ezra settled himself, a hand on each knee, and a queer look of exultation in his eyes, I quickly gathered up my precious dolls in one great armful and carried them into The Room where I hid them on the treadle of the sewing machine. The fringed cover of the machine, a red and gold woven tablecloth, hung to the floor. Ezra had no use for dolls, he had said, he regarded them as idols; his children were not allowed to play with them.

I returned to the kitchen, for I had no intention of losing the explanation for Ezra's well-being which I felt sure was coming; I had never heard him express a feeling of well-being before.

"Wonderful, just wonderful, Mrs. Beattie," he repeated. "The end of the world is at hand."

Ezra was one of many with such a belief. Halley's Comet, about which Adam had spoken, was to appear shortly now to all men, and for certain religious sects, it was deemed to be the forerunner of the Second Coming. Then the righteous would be spared but all others would be consumed by the fire emanating from its tail, when it touched the earth as they expected it to do. Those who entertained doubts as to their holy qualifications in the sight of their God began to consider some means of protection from the wrath to come.

Ezra, despite his saintly calling, turned out to be one of these. Ezra was afraid of God. "He lifts up his eyes to the hills," my father said, "but help does not come; it is a pitiful case."

"I am saved, Frank," he told my father, "because I believe in the Lord. But when the heat of hell passes over the earth, it will touch me, Frank, for I am not purified. There is

63

sin in me. Perhaps there is a way of escape for me and for others like me. Some have seen the fire of hell, and even although they are redeemed, they are afraid of it."

"I tried to talk to him about the mercy of God, but he has his own view of his Creator, and I can't say that it is a very kindly one," my father told us. "What the fellow has in mind, I don't know. I sometimes think that he must have been guilty of a serious offence when he was young and that this preaching he does is an attempt to escape from the consequences. He doesn't feel forgiven, anyway, and yet he preaches forgiveness. It's not easy to make him out."

It was April, a dreamy April with days of unusual warmth at the very beginning before we saw Ezra again. The sky was often filmed over with a thin layer of misty cloud and through it as the sun set, a soft pale flush of pink crept behind the clouds, reaching from horizon to horizon. At night the stars seemed far away and unreal.

In spring of 1910, Ezra rented a small house at a curving corner of our road that led through an enormous gravel pit into open land above the bank of a wide stream.

"He tells me his wife and children are coming to live there," my father said. "He has bought a cow and a horse and buggy. He acts very queer as if he's ashamed of something. I don't know what he's up to."

My father had been on a trip to town. He came driving Big Tom up the hill at dusk. I was watching for him. He saw me and stopped the democrat to help me clamber in for a ride of a few yards through the lane. I climbed down to open the gate for him and to help unhitch Tom and lead him to the watering trough.

Mother had been setting the milk to chill and came from the milk house to greet us.

"You're late, Frank, I put your supper in the oven to keep warm for you. Jean's in the house. Lill has gone to visit Mary Hobbs. She's staying with Joe and Sophia."

Joe and Sophia Hilborn owned the grist mill near the

village and Mary was their niece. She and Lill were bosom friends.

"Yes, I'm late," my father said. "Has Ezra been around?"

"About four o'clock and again about six. His face was flushed; he asked for you but didn't say what he wanted. He was riding a horse, bare-back, the first time. The next time, he came half-running, and left the same way. Have you any idea what's the matter?"

"I'm suspicious. Wait till I put Tom in the stable and give him a bite. Jessie, run ahead and open the stable door; I don't suppose any of the men are handy." Our men usually scattered after supper and chore time was over. My brother Al had strolled off through the fields with his rifle in search of groundhogs, and Will was in the tool-house working on some invention.

When my father had washed and was seated at the table, Mother, Jean and I sat down too, to hear what he had to tell.

There was a small section of bush on Ezra's plot of land, he said, running back from the edge of the gravel pit to another cave-like pit facing it back to back. Once an escaped convict had hidden there for days without being discovered. "I stopped at the blacksmith shop because Tom had a loose shoe," my father said. "While Robbie tightened it he told me that Ezra had attempted to hire a wagon from him, saying he wanted to move some gravel. Rob hadn't a wagon to lend, and he tried to get Ezra to borrow from somebody else. From me, Rob said, but Ezra backed down, said he didn't really need the wagon, and went home. That was at noon.

"He was very queer acting, Robbie said, and asked if Rob wasn't afraid to meet his God? Rob had used a rough word or two. Rob snapped back that he met his God every day and said his prayers, too, like any decent civilized man. He accused Ezra of preaching religion as if he was a saint and everybody else a sinner. Ezra amazed him by losing control of himself, Rob said. He put his face into his hands and his shoulders shook. He turned his back and set off for home."

65

My father chewed a crust from a wheaten loaf of Mother's making, with hurried enjoyment. "When I've had a bite of supper," he said, "I'm driving up to see Ezra. I left the harness on Tom. There must be something wrong."

Jean sighed. "Why you worry about that character, I don't know," she said. "I wish he would move away and stay away. His wife doesn't mix with other women in the community and the children never play with other children, nor go to school, although the boy's six and the girl is seven. Now with the comet looked for and all the queer people acting more queer, one can expect almost anything of Ezra."

My father had very expressive dark eyes which could chastise one severely without him speaking a word. He looked soberly at Jean. "You're right," he said, "but that's why we need to worry about him. He's not alone in his strange fears. In town, today, a man was preaching on the corner of the street – warning everybody who passed by about the comet and that the world is coming to an end. It probably will, but the Almighty isn't telling anybody when. I heard one fellow whispering to another that his neighbour was digging a pit in the ground to hide himself from the wrath of God. What he said made me think of Ezra. He keeps telling me how lucky he is to be living near a gravel pit and that he's making a store-house behind it for his vegetables. I begin to wonder. . . ."

"Why, Father?"

"Because the sect he belongs to is certain that fire will pass over everything on earth. That the world will be purified and left to them – if they are saved, as Ezra says. But some like Ezra have doubts and intend to hide themselves."

It was late when my father returned from visiting Ezra. I heard the clump of Big Tom's feet entering the lane but I was in bed and must wait until morning to hear the news. Or must I? Mother and my brothers and sisters were still below, and as one of the family, surely I had equal rights with them!

The stair to the second floor could be entered by two

different doors with two steps leading to them, from The Room on one side and from what was called The Back Room on the other side – my parents' bedroom and once mine; but now I was a "big" girl and slept upstairs.

I crept soundlessly down the stairs and sat on the bottom step. The Room door was open. The landing between the two exits was covered with linoleum, icy cold in the early spring. I placed the bottom of my nightgown under my feet. I could hear but I couldn't be seen.

My father was talking low and seriously. "When I got there," he said, "I couldn't find anybody. There wasn't even a light in the house, but I could see a spark now and then down by the trees in front of the cave that Ezra had told me about. Several evergreens grow along the path toward it – and at first I thought the spark was a firefly among the branches. Then I heard low voices. I followed the path and found Ezra and his wife, a sickly looking young woman. They must have heard my footsteps on the gravel for they had stopped at the entrance. Their arms were full of parcels. Ezra struck a match and lit the lantern he was carrying.

" 'Good night, folks,' I said. 'Don't let me interfere with your work, if you're busy.'

"Ezra stammered – I never heard him stammer before. He said they wouldn't be a minute and they went on into the cave. I waited. I could see that a pile of stones had been dumped by the side of what you might call the door. There was a cement mixing board lying on the ground beside them. I was certain I could hear a cow bawling and the sound didn't come from the stable. Then I heard a child crying. Both sounds came from the cave.

"I took a few steps nearer and I could see that somebody had started building a stone wall on the far side of the cave entrance; then I saw the whole set-up by the lantern light, for Ezra was standing inside holding the lantern in his hand. There were bundles and barrels everywhere. A cow was tied to a stake in one corner. In another on a shakedown lay the

67

two children, huddled together and crying. Barrels of water lined the place. He hadn't forgotten anything but his trust in the Lord. You could read his intentions. He would wall up the opening until there was just room to crawl in and fix the last stones in place. He had enough food and water for themselves and the cow for several days, I imagine. The horse wasn't included. It had no particular usefulness and there wasn't really space for it.

"How long he'd been preparing, goodness knows. I pitied the man as I looked at him, but when I heard the whimpering of those frightened young ones, my pity kind of withered. 'Did you want to see me?' I asked him.

"He hung up the lantern on a heavy wire extended from a root of cedar to a spike driven into another root before he answered me. Then he faced me. 'Yes,' he said, 'You've been good to me, Frank; there's room for you in here with us if you will come. You and the missus. I'm afraid there isn't room for anybody else.' I felt shivery and hot by turns – the shivers were from a kind of horror that man could be guilty of shaming his Creator with such a view of Him, and the hotness from anger that one person would consider himself worth more than others and leave them to destruction.

"I didn't answer him. I was afraid of what I might say, and who was I to condemn him? There's dozens like him, I hear, digging caves for themselves to hide in until the fire they expect passes. Well, by tomorrow night they'll be digging themselves out again, for when we stepped from the cave, there it was, brighter than any star and with a healthy tail for everybody to see. Ezra dropped to his knees, and I left him there to feel shame and come to his senses."

But by the time my father had finished speaking, everyone had left him. On the veranda we stood staring at Halley's Comet while my father finished his tea before joining us. Mother smiled at me beside her in my nightgown; then seeing that I was barefoot, she untied her apron and placed it on the floor of the veranda for me to stand on.

68

❦ Akra and Dikra ❦

Every summer, just as young leaf was becoming full foliage, a woman peddler appeared around the bend of our road and laboured up the hill. From the time I was a small child until I was eleven, the woman was Akra, a Syran, strong of body and untroubled by the weight of telescope valises which she balanced on either side, holding onto the hard leather of carrier handles with firm grip. Her hands were large and very muscular. Sometimes it frightened me to look at them, remembering stories which I had read about men and women with such powerful hands that they could not resist the destruction of others.

Akra always wore black, with a black shawl sometimes fastened over her head, sometimes – if the weather were hot – draped around her shoulders. Then one could see her sleek dark hair which was parted in the centre and drawn smoothly back into a full coil at the nape of the neck. Her eyes were dark, too, and heavily shadowed, with a sombre expression in them. She rarely smiled and yet her speech was sometimes touched with a dry humour.

The year I was eleven, Akra ceased to come. . . . She was replaced later in the summer by another Syran woman, younger but otherwise not unlike her in appearance, and her name had the same soft ending. Dikra was smaller in every way but with a full, voluptuous figure; her voice was deep and somehow sweeter than Akra's had been. It was an exciting moment when I first heard her speak my plain Scottish name – "Jessie" – pronouncing it "Jarcie". My elder sister Jean so liked the variance, that she adopted the habit of calling me Jarcie, too.

Peddlers preferred to sit on our veranda rather than inside, for there they found plenty of space to display their wares. They were always welcomed by Mother with a cup of tea and "a bite", usually homemade scone or loaf cake, while I would run to the field or garden to tell my father that the vendor had arrived.

He was the Syran women's best customer; while Dikra sat beside her packs, my father would stand where the merchandise could be most easily seen. When he first appeared, Dikra would get to her 'feet, never extending her hand, perhaps because to her this would have indicated an equality, but making outward gestures with one or both, as part of a bow kept only for him.

Doubtless Dikra believed that my father held the purse as did most men in the country, but it was really Mother who made the final decisions as to what should be bought, although always seeking his approval, and allowing him to do the ordering.

I was somewhat embarrassed by the size and evidence of Dikra's great breasts, unrestrained, and although shrouded in black, with the appearance of being emphasized rather than concealed. When she used her hands to demonstrate, she held them at breast level and I, though only a child, blushed a little that she should thus attract attention to her womanhood. But I was fond of Dikra and I tried to believe that her gestures were not intentionally immodest.

Both she and Akra made a serious and difficult business of undoing their telescopes, and never accepted assistance. The heavy straps were fastened by great metal buckles which yielded slowly even to strong fingers. Dikra made a moaning sound as she worked, it may be to gain sympathy from us who, by our purchases could lighten her burden. The moans increased my interest. I held my breath until the covers were removed and I could see what lay inside.

One telescope contained many household supplies, as well as common drugs available without a doctor's prescription. My father liked the rough hand-cleaner packed in tin cans, the production of which, Dikra declared, was achieved by herself from an "old country" recipe. Then there were liniments for man and beast and strong brown and black cough drops which my father fancied, although Mother warned him yearly that they were likely to increase his tendency toward a stomach ulcer. He was usually submissive if Mother protested but when a child approached him we noted that he was seldom without a few of the coughdrops to offer.

There were also dress patterns cut from sturdy brown paper with a pencilled sketch of the style on the outside, gaudy-covered picture books for children, and a few copies in hard cover of the New Testament in English and also in German, for ours was a community of many Mennonites. In a small padded box carefully placed in one corner, were several delicately strung rosaries. There was something for everyone.

The second pack was the more exciting, topped as it was by lengths of dress material; velvets, silks, woollens and cottons. We all peered closer as Dikra opened this display. My father bought at least one dress length yearly for each of his "girls" which included Mother. Mother sometimes shook her head at him, especially when he added half-yards of bright silks selected by me to make dresses for my beloved dolls, for I adored to sew. But Dikra smiled confidently all the while, knowing that he would have his generous way in the end, and that everyone would be happy. Her great dark eyes would light up like lamps in caverns as she totalled my father's bill and looked at him with affectionate respect.

"Missus, you have good, kind husband," she would say in an audible whisper to Mother, knowing full well that the object of her approval could hear, and my father would give Jean or Lill or me a sly wink, pay his debt and settle down beside Mother on the long bench against the wall to hear the story with which Dikra always concluded her transactions.

From Akra we had learned about the small island country of Syra, a place little known, located in the Greek Archipelago. She said she had grown tired of life there, and

72

with another girl had stowed away on a Greek vessel bound for America, only to be discovered a short distance from port by a young sailor who declared their presence to his captain. The ship had turned back but before they had reached land the sailor had fallen in love with Akra and had come later to Syra to marry her. A year afterward the young couple had emigrated to America and with them the other girl, Dikra, posing as Akra's sister.

We had not learned Dikra's story from Akra and therefore it was the more exciting now. Dikra had found employment in Halifax, soon after landing, in a restaurant owned by two Greek brothers who knew Akra's husband. Dikra had married the younger brother after six months of acquaintance, only to find that he was very discontented and bent upon returning home. But it took time to collect sufficient money for passage and meanwhile Dikra tried to encourage him to stay in this land which offered more opportunity. Two children were born and both died from some queer epidemic that affected the heart, Dikra said. The father blamed the Canadian climate.

"He hate this country more every day," she told us. "One day he tell me if I won't go away with him, he will leave me, but then he find that there is only enough money for one anyway. He get ready to go and say he will send for me." But he did not send for Dikra and she did not hear of him again, until after the passing of several years. Then the older brother had admitted to Dikra that he had learned from his parents that her husband had never reached his home.

"He is good man and love me," Dikra told us. "Always he say that he love me too much. That he suffer for love. But he love his own country more than he love wife. He must see it again to be happy. Maybe he fall into ocean or some man kill him in fight. But when I am dreaming he come to me and beg me believe in him, and wait for him. I wait until I die."

At this point none of us attempted to conceal our tears, and Dikra, encouraged by our sympathy, cried, also. "I love

73

my country, too," she declared, "and I wish I never leave."

The love of country must have been implanted deeply in the hearts of the Syrans, for there was little to be had of riches, or opportunity for material progress on the island. At one time, she said, it had been an important calling place for Turkish, Greek and Australian ships, but gradually the few industries there had fallen into desuetude, and the thirty-three thousand population had dwindled to ten thousand.

The land was poor, Dikra explained, and very rocky, covered in many places with a sticky scrub growth of no use to anyone, not even the poor sheep and goats who roamed in search of pasturage among the rocks. Emigration had been from necessity rather than from choice for many, and the sad, defeated inhabitants had left Syra grieving that it had to be.

"The crust in happy place make hunger go," Dikra would say, "but people still hungry with big loaf in strange land. I am hungry every day. I go back to Syra like my man say he go to Greece, if I can."

She had been the eldest of her family, she said, and wondered what had happened to her brothers and sisters. "I was silly girl to run away," she always ended.

Akra had carried small bags of cheap sweets with her, but Dikra explained that peddlers were no longer permitted to sell candy. Mother had never purchased the sweets from Akra, nor had my father, except the cough drops which were neatly parcelled in sealed wrappers. But each time Akra came, she brought a gift to me – a powdery package of Turkish Delight.

At long intervals I was permitted to visit our village store and to spend the handsome sum of ten cents on a selection of candies which I might choose through the glass of a case in which they lay – licorice sticks, fudge roundabouts, peppermints, humbugs, marshmallow men dipped in chocolate, flavoured wax pipes in a variety of colours, (a substitute for forbidden chewing gum), and lozenges, heart-shaped and bearing on them a few words of love in red colouring. The taste was not very good but the appearance delighted the eye. My favourite sweet was not to be found there.

Sometimes when my father took me to the nearest town with him, we visited a small confectioner's for a dish of ice cream. This cream was served in the shape of a cone on saucers and as it disappeared spoonful by spoonful I looked a little sorrowfully at my father. It was such a rare treat. But in that shop I found my Turkish Delight: a candy which was more than a candy. Father always bought a generous amount, mine, but really for the family.

I was taught to share, but there was something more precious about the packages of the same confection which Akra brought for me. They seemed more particularly my own, although, alas, I was not permitted to taste what they contained.

Mother placed the delicacy in a covered dish and set it high on the cupboard shelf. She managed to include an object lesson in her reason for confiscation of the stuff.

"There is a verse in the Bible," she would tell me gently, "about appearances being deceitful and wolves sometimes wearing sheep's clothing. We don't know what is in this candy nor who made it." Then, when she saw tears in my eyes, "Never mind, dear. When your father goes to town again, I'll tell him to buy you a little bag just for yourself. It doesn't matter about this. It's safer not to eat it, but you can look at it."

But it *did* matter to me for I was sure that Akra's gift had something different about it.

The two Syran women were great friends still, and Dikra, left alone, had gone to live with the older woman and to help her with her many children. Akra's husband was a good man when sober, Dikra said, but he had periods of drunkenness when he would go away for days, even weeks, returning penniless and often physically ill from over-drinking. They had finally moved into central Ontario where work was more plentiful and new friends could be found. Many immigrants had come there from far countries and they were happier than they had been for a long time. Akra did not peddle, now, because she had learned that everyone was more contented if she stayed in the home. Dikra shared profits with her.

The inhabitants of Syra were mostly Roman Catholic but Akra, assisted through her trials by the Salvation Army, had become one of the Army women. To become a Protestant, to Dikra, was to be forever lost and sometimes she lay awake all night, she said, praying fervently for her friend's return to the faith.

Dikra's last visit occurred the summer that my father had added a young Armenian to our men. In broken English he had explained that he was afraid to take work in a town because he was an escapee from Turkish Armenia where a number of horrible massacres had taken place. "He seems to think that they are still after him from over there," my father said. "I can't understand exactly what it was all about in his case, but it appears that he was one of three survivors in a massacre of two hundred high school boys. The three boys pretended to be dead and after lying still among the bodies of their schoolmates until the Turks had gone, crawled to safety. Somehow he made his way with the other two to the coast and finally to Canada. When he learns to speak our language better, no doubt he'll want to tell us more."

My father had met the young man when taking a stroll along our road one spring evening.

"He showed plainly that he was searching for work," my father told us, and needing another hand, he had hired him. When we asked his name, it was difficult to make it out but it sounded like Arran. And Arran he was, as long as he was one of us.

Arran worked well, was quick to learn, and seemed quite contented, although he could not speak to the other workmen. However, unlike Freddie, even without a knowledge of English, he knew when to laugh and when to keep quiet and the men liked him.

Dikra had told us of a younger brother, only ten when she left Syra, who had been adopted by an Armenian trader and taken away from the island. Her parents had agreed to the adoption because the trader was a fine man and rich who had promised to educate their son and to teach him the business. This was indeed an opportunity for a Syran boy whose family was very poor. The trader promised that the son would become a rich man like himself one day, and that he would bring him home for a visit after a few years. Perhaps, then the entire family could emigrate to Armenia, he said.

"It is one of the wonders of the world," my father said, "the way the Almighty manoeuvres things to bring our lives into the direction He has planned for them, whatever we may do. Nobody would be inclined to believe it, if you told them that a peddler woman from Syra who left her country years ago and hadn't seen sight or heard sound of her family since that time, would find one of them hoeing potatoes in Canada."

But that is what happened to Dikra as she left our door after her last visit, and made her way along the road through our peaceful countryside. She stopped to rest for a minute in the shade of a pine tree which grew close to the fence. In the field, on a sandy slope partly shaded by the same tree, Arran was working faithfully. Why he looked up as Dikra stopped, why he peered closely at her and she back at him, what in her appearance drew him to recognize her, he could not tell us.

Only Mother saw their meeting, for my father had gone back to his work in the hay field, and my sisters and I into the house. My brothers and our other men were busy elsewhere. Only Mother, her heart sympathetic toward the woman struggling forward with her load. Mother had stepped outside to watch Dikra on her way, perhaps to wave a hand if she looked back.

"They came running with their arms around each other

to tell me," she said. "Dikra left her two valises sitting by the roadside until I reminded her; then Arran ran to get them. At first I wondered, could it be that she had found her long lost husband? But the boy was too young for that! There is so much in life we don't understand," she went on, "That the woman and the boy should meet in such a way and know each other! I can't think that it happened by accident."

"It didn't," my father said.

Plans were discussed that night with Dikra acting as interpreter. Arran offered to stay if we needed him, but everyone agreed that he should have a few days holiday at least, to enjoy the reunion. He accepted his freedom to go with his dark eyes shining. Mother prepared a shakedown for Dikra on the parlour floor, because there was not an empty bed in the house, and when morning came the brother and sister were up with the sun and on their way.

"He come back to you," Dikra told my father before leaving. "He want to come and I want him to come. Good people . . . good people. . . ."

Arran came back, but when summer waned and the need for extra help was over, he went to live with Akra and Dikra. Dikra found work in a restaurant and Arran with a pick and shovel. "The woman's eyes – you wouldn't recognize them – they're so happy," my father reported, after going to investigate their circumstances. "And you'd think the boy's shovel was a golden spade."

But I missed the woman peddler's visits, for she came no more; and it was with satisfaction that I learned later that Turkish Delight is indeed the native candy of Syra.

CHAPTER
9

One bright spring morning when the silver of the poplars was beginning to show green, and the tangle of vine and shrub along the stump fences was brightening with raspberry blossom, pink creeper bells, and the mauve of milkweed, from a jagged point of pine standing by the fence side, I heard the rare song of the indigo bunting.

Mother and I were making our way along the road to what we called The Upper Gate, with a mid-morning snack of tea and soda bread for our men. This gate led into about twenty-five acres of the farm which my father set apart for market gardening. Our greenhouses stood just inside the fence, and from there the land dipped down gently to a hollow of perhaps fifty rods in length and about the same in width. This hollow was dark with loam and suitable for celery growing. Eastward the land rose gently again into berry patches, finally stretching level in fields of corn and potatoes, the corn glistening in the sun.

The low-lying land of rich black loam had been gutted into deep wide furrows evenly crossing it from east to west. The furrows were formed by a wooden plough built for the purpose by my brother Will whose ability to invent had solved many a problem.

Our men were straddling the rows on their knees, that morning, for it was late-celery planting time.

"Hear that little bird," Mother said to me. "I don't remember hearing it since the summer little Bella died."

My sister Isabella, at three years, had died of "dipthetic croup" before I was born, but her memory was kept evergreen by Mother in conversation with us. My father listened in silence when Mother spoke of her. She had been his darling, Mother said. I was now his darling, I believed, but I was not jealous of the golden-haired little sister who had lived so short a time.

"And that was the year, too, that they found poor Henry," Mother added.

Henry Dree, now married and no longer living in the nearby community, had at one time been a most unhappy young man. His own mother, "a sensible woman in most ways," Mother explained, had believed that the child born to her with a club foot had been sent as a curse by the Almighty. Although kind to her other children, even to Minnie of the hair lip, Mrs. Dree had openly shown her distaste for this one of her own flesh and blood. "It didn't affect Henry much, until he came to thirteen," Mother said, "and then he got dour and moody so that he didn't attend to his lessons at school and stayed by himself in the school yard. The boys tried to coax him into games, too, and were kind enough to him. That summer he ran away. Jimmie had done his best to be a good father to the boy but with the mother taking the attitude she did, it was pretty hard, and Henry had begun to act as if he disliked his father as much as he did his mother. He wouldn't speak when spoken to, nor have anything to do with his brother and sisters. Nobody outside really knows how much was said against him before his face, but there must have been enough to make him feel he was not wanted."

Jimmie Dree had come to my father when the boy was missing for a night and a day, and together they had driven over the country roads looking and asking if he had been seen. "If Henry hadn't been found," Mother told us, "I doubt if Jimmie would have lived very long; for he turned away from food and couldn't sleep at nights. He was always sturdy before, but then he became thin and poorly, and nobody ever heard him laugh until Henry was home again."

It was September, Mother said, when a farmer taking grain to be ground into flour at the Dundas mill, while passing through the Beverley Swamp, heard a moaning among the heavy growth of bushes and trees by the roadside. He

81

stopped his team and investigated. There, lying at the foot of a cedar tree, clinging to a bough with both hands while suction from the bog tried to claim him, was Henry.

He had been gone for almost two months, Mother said, but no one had thought of looking for him in the dread Swamp which was known to be a place of danger in more ways than one. He had lived in an old shack that some wayfarer had built to shelter himself, and had managed to keep alive on what food he could find – berries, tasty herbs and the meat of small animals. "He was almost a skeleton," Mother recalled, "but sick in no way except in his mind, poor fellow. Yet he cared enough about living to try to hold himself above ground when the bog made to suck him under. That was a good sign, and when the farmer managed to persuade him to ride out of the place on his wagon, that was another."

After finding out who the boy was, the farmer had insisted on taking him to his father. No one ever learned what passed in the Dree house that night, but Jimmie came with Henry to see my father a few days later and asked if he would take Henry to work for him in the market garden.

"It was only a nice walk home at night," Mother said, "but we all thought it best if Henry stayed here. We gave him the room that Freddie had last summer. At first he was silent the way he had been at home, but we treated him like one of the family as much as we could, and it was little Bella who made him want to live, I think. She loved the boy and when he came from the garden for meals, she would run to the door and clap her hands and say, 'Come and have some nice pudding, Henry.' And when he had washed and was ready for the table, she would take his hand and walk there with him. Then she would come out of The Room and sit on a chair smiling to herself, just as if she knew what she was doing for him. And perhaps she did."

After little Bella died, Mother said that Henry had shown signs of becoming morose again, and knowing his grief, our men had sympathy for him, and tried to make him feel that he was one of them. One day the family doctor who had been called to examine my brother Al, ill with an appendix attack, had noticed Henry and talked to my father about him. The doctor had explained that the nature of the deformity was such that Henry could be fitted with special boots which would help him to walk normally. Jimmie was consulted, and in the spring Henry was taken to a hospital in Toronto where he remained for some time for treatment and fitting.

"When he was married," Mother said, "you couldn't notice that he was crippled at all. It was a happy marriage, too. The girl came to work for a neighbour, and she was the shy, plain kind. Henry had gone back home because Jimmie needed him and the trouble with his mother was somehow over. The girl was picking wild raspberries in the winterberry swamp behind the farm when Henry first saw her, they said. He had gone to the swamp for the cows which watered there in a crossing brook, and one of the herd had made for the girl. She had screamed and Henry had hurried as fast as he could to rescue her. The cow had attempted to gore him with its sharp horns but he had managed to ward it off and to help the girl over logs and rough ground to the fence. There they sat together to get their breath and there the romance started."

"It is wonderful how nature brings the right people together," my father put in. "They needed just the sort of companionship they found in each other. Henry might have been very unhappy if he had married a girl who thought herself better than he was. When they moved away to Alberta, where Henry bought up some ranch land, the country folks were sorry to see them go. Not many of them remembered about Henry's trouble when he was a boy."

The Beverley Swamp was a few miles southeast of our farm. It had covered an area of ten thousand acres, part of which had been cleared and drained to make fertile farm land. The swamp had been greatly feared by travellers and settlers alike and although now open country for some distance along the road leading through it from Galt to Hamilton, no one driving there could forget that many had entered never to be seen again.

Originally built of heavy corduroy, the road led over patches of grey quicksand where, even when drained, the earth looked menacing and ugly.

One June day after Mother told me the story of Henry, my father took me with him in the buggy to visit my Aunt Mary who lived in Hamilton, an overnight trip usually made once a year and in the summer season. It was Mother's habit to go along but on that occasion she and my sisters were deep in preserving strawberries, and my father and I were alone.

Aunt Mary was Mother's youngest sister, a dainty matron with long, thick hair which formed a crown of gold on a head always held high and proudly. Aunt Mary had young ways although the mother of four sons and two daughters varying in ages from a toddler to early youth. Her toilet was never complete without a dash of powder and a touch of eau de cologne. Such accessories were not as yet to be found in our household. Mother had a dislike for perfumes, "except the natural kinds," she used to say. The natural kinds to which she referred were the scent of a flower or of some familiar foliage plant, the air on a spring morning, or its softer fragrance at dusk. Even my sisters, although now young women, depended upon cleanliness and, perhaps, a homemade hand lotion containing a few drops of rose water, or a sprig of scented geranium concealed in the bosom as an added allurement.

Aunt Mary, to me, was therefore of a different world. It was always an event to visit her and to enjoy her wholewheat drop biscuits and fresh stewed fruit sweetened with brown sugar or honey.

As we entered the road through the Swamp, I crept

closer to my father on the buggy seat. Where fields now lay, even in June the indentations and the grooves between furrows held water. Except in the driest weather water crept up to the trunks of trees through masses of swamp grass and rushes. At one time the Swamp had sheltered wild beasts and rattlesnakes. It had hummed above the bogs with flies and mosquitoes. But none of its dangers compared with that of the grey stretches of sand which appeared, my father said, as if they had risen purposefully before the human eye could detect them quickly enough to avoid their treacherous sucking mouths.

Remembering, my father guided Old Tom and our buggy cautiously over the fitted logs, although he said, "There's no danger, now, you know. But before the road was drained you were onto the evil places before you knew it, and once on, it was good-bye."

In pioneer days, he said, the nearest grist mill for use of the farmers in North Dumfries was established at Dundas. Many travelled the Swamp road on foot, carrying a sack of grain and returning with a sack of flour. "They were lucky," he said, "if they didn't meet some sort of trouble along the way. There was more to worry them than wild beasts and snakes and quicksand. A few men hid themselves here to escape the law, risking their lives to save their lives, as it were. Like Henry, they stayed out of sight and lived on whatever wild meat they could get. The Swamp had big patches of strawberries and raspberries, too, and wild plum and cherry trees. Oh they managed all right. One man lived in hiding for five years. He had come from distant parts and was wanted for some sort of suspected wickedness. It turned out that he was innocent, though, but he died from the effect of slinking and dodging for such a long time. Poor fellow, by the end of it, he probably believed that he really was guilty. We get to thinking wrong when we live wrong. What are you crying for, Jessie?"

I had not known that I was crying. I wiped the tears away with my hand. "I was feeling sorry for that man, I guess," I said.

It was impossible to forget that the Swamp led above the graves of its early victims. One story often told about it and thought to be mere legend was proved to be nothing of the sort, but cold fact, when a farmer digging a post hole many years after discovered the wheel of a cart in common use in early times.

The soldiers of the king were stationed in various parts of Canada, then. The headquarters for a regiment might be in one town and part of the regiment on duty somewhere else. This was true of a regiment in Galt with a company placed in Dundas.

"Every so often," my father told me as we jogged along, that June day, "maybe once a month for all I know, money to pay the men outside the headquarters was taken by cart in a strong box to wherever they were. From Galt to Dundas was such a dangerous trip that an officer always accompanied the paymaster. Robbers hiding in the swamp would know the box contained a lot of money. One day the major set off with the paymaster. They were well into the Swamp when the horse stopped. It was a trusted animal and certainly not tired, for the distance was reasonable. The paymaster, who was driving, tried to force the horse on but it wouldn't go. It was late in the afternoon and kind of misty by that time – hard to see because fog had settled over the roadway. The major declared the horse was balky and began to whip it alongside but the paymaster begged him not to do it. He felt sure, he said, that something was wrong and that the creature was trying to tell them. The major laughed at him and swore at the horse which reared in the shafts but it wouldn't budge.

"The major ordered the paymaster off the cart and threatened to charge him with insubordination. Then he whipped the animal unmercifully, until it went on. About three feet forward, horse, cart, strongbox, and the major sank into the earth. The paymaster tried to help the officer to get free, but he had become entangled in the long reins and there was no hope for him. The paymaster ran back many miles to report the tragedy."

But there were happier stories of the vast bushland also – of summer days when my father and his brothers had ventured into its dense and tangled undergrowth in search of the biggest raspberries known to grow wild in any part of the country. "And to shy clear of the biggest spiders," laughed my father; "they were black and yellow spotted and had enormous eyes. Harmless, no doubt, for I never heard tell of anyone being bitten, but they were fierce enough looking to scare us away from the most tempting berry patch."

Before corduroy was laid to form a road, travellers driving or on foot always carried a hatchet or an axe because often they had to cut their way through the underbrush, always on the watch for those patches of grey quicksand.

"Since it was almost impossible then to travel through with any peace of mind," my father recalled, "a number of boats – eighty feet long and sixteen feet wide – seven of them, called *The Fleet of Arks* were built to carry grain and other produce by the Grand river to towns on the other side of the Swamp, especially to Dundas where the boats reloaded with barrels of flour – four hundred to a boat – which they brought back for sale. The only time the boats could be used was in the spring when the water was high. Then one year a boat was wrecked on the way down and after that the *Arks* weren't used. Men took to travelling by the Swamp again."

I was glad when we were through the Swamp and on our way into the pleasant rolling country. My father's words were always the same when we left the Swamp behind: "Well, it didn't get us this time." The words were accompanied by a sigh of relief although we both knew that the period of danger was long past. Then my father would laugh and put his big hand over the two of mine which he did not know were clasped together in fear. For the haunting threat of the place went with me, the rankness of smell, still apparent, the indescribable unseen ugliness that still existed below, although man had control, now. Even the evergreens and hardwood trees, maples, oaks and beeches, growing in great strength because of the bountiful moisture, seemed unfriendly, and the flat fields of the cleared portion, now drained and in crop, were still only the concealment of tragedy to me.

But I would not have missed our journeys through the Beverley Swamp nor the stories so graphically told, indeed I would not; however I was glad when Old Tom gave added speed to the buggy wheels as the road improved, and when my father hummed a little tune, for these were indications that we were once again in a friendly world. I began to taste in anticipation the special kind of apple sauce, seasoned with spices and sweetened with brown sugar, which only Aunt Mary knew how to make.

❧ The Country Doctor ❧

Dusk was falling. The sun had all but set, flushing back in orange brilliance from behind the Pinnacle Hill into the darkening blue of the evening sky. Autumn had come. The foliage of the fruit trees in the orchard was already tinting yellow, russet and brown with here and there a dash of red or purple. The night was without wind.

A first star had appeared eastward, cool, shafted. There would be a moon, later, but for the present only the after-glow of the sunset and the silver of the star lightened the twilight.

The air had a crisp chill in it and on days when the wind passed, there was a shudder of apprehension in the Lombardy poplars and in the paling elm that grew at the west side of the house.

I sat under a sweet apple tree in the orchard. I had been walking up and down watching the sky and listening for the turn of wheels. A rubber-tired open buggy now stood by our houseyard gate, a sorrel mare was tethered to our hitching post. From the northwest window of the house, a lamp threw an unsteady glimmer, indicating that it was not stationary but that someone was holding it aloft.

That would be Jean, I thought, holding it near the bedside for the doctor to better see his patient. Then a tall figure temporarily blotted out the light, crossing the room to the other side. After that, the hand holding the lamp moved from view and there was only an oblong of yellow marking the window in the dark wall.

I began to walk up and down again between the rows of trees. With tears restrained, I prayed earnestly.

My brother Al had come stumbling from the corn field that afternoon where he had been picking and hulling. He came half-doubled over with pain. My father was quickly summoned from the potato patch where the men were digging. He hitched our fastest single horse to the buggy and prepared to take Al into town to consult the doctor. But Al had proved too ill for travelling and my father had then set off for the village where a telephone line now reached. The doctor had agreed to come at once.

It was almost five miles to town and although the doctor's sorrel mare was nimble-footed, the time of waiting had seemed endless. But now all would be well, I thought, with a faith in this man which was shared by many. When he appeared from the door carrying his small black satchel, my father went with him to the gate. I felt sure that my brother was safe, and I ran to the house.

Mother met me with a sober face. She had been weeping. Al, it seemed, had had another attack of appendicitis, so severe that the doctor had urged an operation.

Before long a queer-looking vehicle (closed-in and drawn by two horses) drove through the yard gateway. The driver stood at the head of the horses to assure that they would remain motionless while my father and one of our men carried my brother from the house and placed him inside on a stretcher.

Al's voice, vibrating with pain and fear called to me, "Good-bye, Jessie," and my father lifted me in his arms for a last look. It was a tragic moment.

As the vehicle rolled away down the hill with my father sitting beside the driver, we were all crying. An appendix operation was rarely performed in those days and of eight undertaken at the local hospital during the year it was reported only two patients had survived.

My brother did not die. He was one of the lucky ones, my father said, adding that more than luck was responsible. Each evening the old farm house had been silent while my father read from the Bible and prayed, a usual event but now with a special significance.

That was a difficult autumn for my father. Will had left the farm to train for a career in engineering. Al came home suffering from complications. It was January before the sorrel mare ceased to toss snow from under its nimble feet as it came regularly up our hill. Al remained thin and pale for most of that winter and my father kept two extra farm hands, for Al was not even capable of light chores. Twice weekly, in fascinated horror, I saw him swallow a long rubber tube. The tube had a funnel on the outer end into which Jean poured liquid from a tall pitcher. The funnel was then dipped down into a basin and the solution returned. When I asked what was happening, Mother explained that my brother was washing out his stomach.

When spring came, affairs in our family returned to normal and Al took his place among the other men again while my father praised the great skill and the conscientious care which the doctor had provided.

The doctor was a busy man, but after that winter, he seldom passed our gate without stopping for a chat with my father. They became fast friends. I was a sickly child and when his attention was turned to me I felt healed by his very presence. Tall, handsomely built, with eloquent kindly dark eyes, in my estimation he was a hero among men.

"I'm glad that he concerns himself with animals as well as with people," my father said, when the sorrel mare won first prize in the single class at the Galt Horse Show that spring. "It makes for a more merciful kind of nature."

What my father meant, I think, was that the doctor's concern for the betterment of life in any form showed that he did not apply himself to his profession only for the pride of achievement and for material gain.

His views were firm and progressive as was shown in his fight against the majority when a matter of principle was at stake. "He practices ideals as well as medicine," my father said. "The fellow who tries to wheedle, gets nowhere with him."

An example of the doctor's resolute character was shown when he openly disagreed with my father over a matter of quarantine. It happened the year that I came home from school with the announcement, "Millie Jones has got the Scarlet Fever."

Mother paled. "My goodness," she said. "And they've such a big family, it will likely go right through the house. When did she come down with it?"

"She was at school yesterday," I explained. "Nobody really knows for sure that it is the fever, yet. They didn't have the doctor, Tommy says, but she has a dreadful sore throat and spots."

"Tommy!" Mother exclaimed. "Was Tommy at school today?"

"Oh yes," I said cheerfully. "And he hopes he won't get it. Mary sleeps with Millie so she's likely to, she thinks. Cora and Ruth sleep in another room."

"All at school?" Mother's voice shook a little.

"Oh yes; but Mary says she won't likely be by tomorrow, and if it wasn't for the sore throat she says she'd be glad. She hates school – especially arithmetic."

Mother had collapsed into a chair. My sisters were upstairs. She called them.

"There's only one thing to do," Lill said firmly, "keep this young one at home."

Jean protested, "But for how long if it goes through that family? And nobody will ever succeed in convincing the Joneses that they should take care of other people. They haven't had a doctor and you can bet they won't have. They'll pretend it's a cold or something and keep on going and coming. But you're right for the present, Lill. We'll keep our Jarcie at home."

I burst into tears. I was not like Mary Jones. I enjoyed going to school. "I can't stay home," I sobbed into Jean's neck, for she had drawn me lovingly to her as soon as she realized the effect of her words on me. "I can't stay home because tomorrow is Arbour Day and we're going to plant a tree and clean the school and the yard. Then we're going to Kinzie's bush. The mayflowers are out and lots and lots of other flowers."

Arbour Day, the first Friday in May, was looked forward to by every child and especially by such as I. In the morning the boys would arrive with rakes, hoes, shovels, clippers, and perhaps a hammer and some nails to repair a gap in the picket fence – and the girls with brooms, buckets, scrub brushes, and cleaning cloths. Soap, Bon Ami, stove blacking and such cleaners were supplied by the school.

It was a proud moment when an older girl was chosen to climb the tall step-ladder to reach the rows of small panes in the big windows, while a boy on a lean-to polished the same window from outside. The task of scrubbing the school floor was allotted to the older girls also, properly clad in canvas sack aprons. Flower beds were dug in the yard and corners rid of dead leaves and rubbish which the wind had gathered there.

Lunch was enjoyed from dinner pails with extra sandwiches and treats provided by mothers for the special day, knowing that appetites would be heartier than usual.

The great moment came when the tree, a maple, was finally planted and with the teacher we gathered around it to sing *The Maple Leaf Forever.*

The walk to the hardwood bush was half a mile along a winding road. The road dropped into a valley, crossed a trout stream, and climbed up again. We left the road at the stream after tossing wishing stones from the wooden bridge, and entered a clover field, a pasture behind the clover, an avenue of saplings, and then clambered over or through a snake fence into the woods.

The plentiful wild flowers of late spring were now there waiting. Brown leaves crumbled beneath our feet giving off a pleasant dry sweet smell. We avoided stepping on plants which in some places forced their stems through a loosened patch or pushed the leaves aside. The fresh fragrance of new foliage and of flowers mingled with the scent of the dead leaves. Delicacy was found beside some old stump, or at the root of a shading tree, in a clump of dainty hepaticas. Our young hearts praised the day, our pulses quickened.

Wild flowers were so plentiful then that we were not discouraged from gathering them. But the boys were too busy chasing the runaway squirrel or rabbit, or cutting themselves whistles from thick stems of greening willow. The joyous cries of the girls mingled with the shouts of the boys as the latter neared their prey.

I did not miss Arbour Day.

"They won't be sitting close together in the classroom," Jean argued, "and she's been doing that with them for probably days. I think we should let her go."

"I suppose you're right," Lill admitted. "Perhaps Millie hasn't got the fever anyway, and we can't keep her home forever. If it really is the fever, there will soon be others."

There were others and eventually, in the autumn, there was I.

My bosom friend, Tillie, owned a Shetland pony and a phaeton with a fringed top. Tillie and I had been appointed that autumn by the Union Sunday School in the village to collect for the Bible Society. This was considered an honour. It was easy enough to reach even remote areas of the farming country with the help of Jeff who trotted happily wherever he was encouraged to go, slowly but surely. The amount of each contribution was entered by Tillie in a small black book and the money deposited in a beaded leather purse with a pull-cord top.

On Saturday morning Tillie came driving Jeff up our hill about nine o'clock. It was a softly misted September day. I ran out to join her.

There was magic in that day. The sky smiled, the sun warmed us, the fields were tinting with purple and yellow, the trees had begun to array themselves in glory. We stopped for lunch by a water-filled patch of low woodland. The reeds and rushes stood dreaming; a pair of wild ducks floated easily and unfearingly where the water was deepest.

From this hollow, a vine-covered fence led up a gentle slope. Half-way up stood a reddening maple. Under its boughs we settled.

With Tillie's lunch, her mother had packed two saucers full of homemade maple cream candy, and two perfectly ripened Bartlett pears. There were two jellied tarts and two wine-sap apples with mine.

Despite the sunshine and the balmy temperature, there was a hint of frost in the air and when a wind came up, it was chilly. I felt the wind on my back as Tillie and I sat talking and laughing after making the business of eating as long as possible.

"Mama says to bring you home for supper," Tillie told me. "We're having stuffed spare ribs and baked prune pudding." Two favourite dishes of mine especially when made by Tillie's mother who was an excellent cook, yet my palate did not tickle at their mention, that day. My throat did, however, and the tickle became a soreness which was difficult to disguise. My head ached and when a breeze came along, I shivered.

"I feel kind of queer," I admitted finally.

Tillie's wide eyes grew wider. "Oh, my goodness," she said half-sadly, half-exultantly, "maybe you're getting the fever, Jessie. But Aunt Ellie says don't think about a pain and it will go away. I guess the same thing is true about a fever. You'd better try it anyway. And don't say anything at my house, will you? I'm your bosom friend and I've got to look after you whatever you get, and then I've got to get it, too. But Mama mightn't think so."

Mother wouldn't think so either, I felt sure, but I was heartened by such an expression of devotion from one whom I adored.

I went home with Tillie and bravely I partook of the

delicious baked meat and pudding, the latter served with Jersey cream. But I ate sparingly and Tillie's mother was watching.

"You feel sick, Jessie."

I looked at Tillie. She was quicker of thought and word than I. "She's not sick, Mama," she protested. "She just ate too much lunch. Mrs. Beattie sent tons and tons, and they don't have much candy at their house. She didn't leave a speck of the maple cream."

But Tillie's mother spoke to me again, this time in the form of a question.

"Do you feel sick, Jessie?"

With falling tears, I nodded. Then I put my head onto my folded arms.

"I'm going to take her home, Mama," Tillie declared firmly. "I've been with her all day, and I'm going to take her home."

Tillie took me home, urging Jeff to step more quickly than usual while she kept one arm around me. Her touching devotion seemed to heal me, "I'm only a little sick," I said, "and I don't think it's the fever."

It was the fever, but Tillie was not affected.

The next morning, Mother took one look at my chest and sent my father for the doctor.

The dispute between my father and the doctor arose when the latter disagreed with Mother's plans to protect the rest of the family, for no one but she and my father, it seemed, had had the fever. "I'll manage fine, doctor," she said, "I'll stay upstairs and nurse her, and keep everyone away from the room. I'll hang a dipped sheet of formaldehyde across the door and the girls will bring our food and set it in the hall. I won't touch anything going or coming in and out. If it is necessary for me to go any place in the house from the room, I'll wash my hands and put on a covering. The men can go in and out through the kitchen and there's a back stairs to their rooms. . . ."

But the doctor shook his head. "Your intentions are good, Mrs. Beattie," he said, "but they won't give the necessary protection. This house is in quarantine." He turned to my father, "An officer will be out to post the cards, later today. I think we'd better have one on the gate as well as one on the door, because so many come and go here."

My father's dark eyes blazed fire. "Do you mean to say. . . ." he paused.

"Exactly," the doctor said and his voice was firm. "Carelessness has caused Jessie to be exposed to the disease. Carelessness, which risks the loss of life, perhaps in another family, perhaps in your own, is inexcusable. We can't take the chance, Mr. Beattie." They were friends. Indeed they had a brotherly love for one another, but now they stood glaring, or was my father the only one who glared? The doctor's eyes I could not see, but his voice was stern.

"I hear," my father said, "that a half dozen families in this village have the fever, and there's not one in quarantine."

"Exactly," repeated the doctor. "I'll stop at one of the trustee's homes on my way back and request that the school be closed and fumigated."

My father shook his head. "I'm afraid you won't get anywhere," he said. "The disease is under cover and nobody will admit it exists if they think they'll be put to inconvenience and expense."

"But you'll support me."

My father didn't answer. "And perhaps we can find a way to make your problem less," the doctor continued. "You have an empty house on your land."

"I had a married farm hand in it, but he left a month ago."

"Good. With so many people exposed here, why not move Jessie there? With her mother, of course, and a nurse. I have a nurse in mind who will fit in well. Then after ten days your own household can come and go as they please, if there are no more cases, and I don't think there will be."

"It's all silliness," from my father. "This quarantine business."

"You may think that until a delicate child contracts the disease and dies. None of us would want that on our conscience."

My father put out his hand. "You're right," he said, "but the people in this village will hate your guts, Doctor."

"A good beginning for a revolution," the doctor said and smiled.

They went out together.

I heard no more and felt too ill to care what plans were being made. But the thought of moving into another house – I had been born where we now lived! It was frightening and yet exciting.

The doctor and my father were still talking, Mother said. They were standing at the gate. "Still arguing," she said, "but your father is losing; I can tell by the set of his shoulders."

My father was impressed by the reasonableness of the doctor's argument but the school trustees were not. "You and your new-fangled ideas," they snorted. "And besides who knows that anybody else but the Beattie girl has got the fever? No other cases have been reported. You can't force us to fumigate and we're not going to. Doctors used to be doctors but now every case of belly-ache is appendicitis, and every time a youngster has a cold or a simple kind of disease, there's a big fuss; you fellows would make an epidemic out of anything just to get a little publicity. Prove to us that one other child in this village has the fever and we'll call a meeting."

"They knew that I couldn't prove it without invading a family's privacy," the doctor told my father on his next visit. "But you know it and I know it. Let me have the cards put up Mr. Beattie. After the incubation period, if nobody in the house comes down with the disease, we'll take them away."

Plans were already being made to remove Mother and me to the empty house.

"Go ahead and do what you think is best," my father yielded.

They shook hands. "I'm sorry to put you to this inconvenience," the doctor said, "but you're helping forward the movement to detect and control contagious diseases. I need your support in carrying out this duty."

In two days we were settled in the empty house; not empty now, for Mother and a white-capped nurse accompanied me, and my father came to keep guard at night, entering by an end door and sleeping in a room cut off from the part which we occupied.

The place had a ghostly appearance with sheets that had been dipped in disinfectant floating at doorways, and doorknobs swathed in cloths that dripped with a formaldehyde solution. Mother and the nurse washed their hands with a strong-smelling soap every time they touched me or anything in the room. Dishes were boiled and all reading matter, after use, was thrown into a deep can outside and burned.

The rooms which we occupied were on the first floor and every school day Tillie arrived after four to flatten her nose against the outside of my window and to blow kisses to me.

As the days shortened, it was sometimes dark before my father, with a lantern in his hand, came by a short cut across the fields. We could only look at each other through the glass of the window. It was happy news when he announced that the quarantine had been lifted, since no cases among the other members of the family and our men had taken place. Of course the old house had been thoroughly disinfected with pots of stick sulphur burning, followed by a good house-cleaning.

A day came when Tillie arrived at mid-afternoon. Her big blue eyes were excited. "The school's closed," she told me. "Pa says it should have been when Millie got sick, then you wouldn't have got sick nor anybody else. Dolly Ross has complications and they had two doctors and now, Pa says, something will be done. The doors and windows are all closed up but you can smell the awful stuff they have inside to kill the fever when you pass on the road. The old germs are getting dead, Jessie, and nobody else will catch the fever now."

The weeks of isolation finally came to an end. The sheets and the door-knob covers were removed and I was bathed in an evil-smelling solution, clad in fresh, clean clothing brought by my father, and removed from the pest house.

It was a smiling Father who helped Mother and me to seats in the democrat. It was the day of the first snowfall and I was heavily wrapped in blankets. The doctor had come to give me a final examination and to carry the nurse back to town with him. His fine dark eyes were warm with pleasure and victory.

"He's a good man," my father said as we drove away, my hand snuggled into his for the first time in many months. "He's proved his point and won everybody's respect. What he did will bring patients to him, not keep them from him, as we both thought at the start."

I watched the sorrel mare trotting off toward town. The fork in the road took us in an opposite direction. I had two wonderful new friends, I thought, and I would miss them. The doctor had taken the nurse with him.

Then I looked back at the now deserted house. Already our men were piling up the discarded clothing and bedding which, in fear of possible infection, we had left just outside the door. Before we reached the lane gate, a great bonfire lit the sky.

11

The pasture fields were tinting brown and purple with here and there wine and grey stalks of tall weeds appearing. The scene was lightened by patches of growth still green. The corn had reached its full height and the tall, glistening leaves had begun to yellow. Twined around the base of the stalks here and there orange pumpkins looked out. A mistiness in the valleys and a low haze hanging over the ridge of hills in the south indicated that summer was near an end. The air had the scent of drying foliage and sunburned mellow fruit.

It was the last week in August. My father came hurrying in about noon with the news that the threshers had arrived in the district and would probably be coming our way by the following evening.

The threshers – Eph and Bill – were brothers who had a monopoly on threshing operations in the community. Their arrival was a signal for preparations to begin on every farm, because if they found no preparedness, they might pass on to the next neighbour and the dilatory farmer might not be able to persuade them to return to him for some time.

Barn floors were cleared of stored implements and rubbish, granary bins were thoroughly cleaned in preparation for new grain, firewood was piled in a proper location for easy access to the engine tender. The wood had been cut and arranged months before to be dried to a tinder by the sun until bubbles of tasty gum were drawn out of tamarack and pine.

A small window looking into the stable yard was removed to provide an outlet for the pipe which would blow sweet-smelling chaff into a stack clear of the stable entrances.

"They've been busy at Dan O'Neil's since early this

morning," my father announced. "Dan came by to tell me we're next. He thinks they'll be finished with him by tomorrow afternoon. They'll have time to set up here, then, before dark. That means they'll be around for supper, and of course over night. I'll drive into Galt and get a roast of beef and any other stuff you want for the meals, Ma."

It was still summer holidays. I would not miss a single precious moment of threshing-time, thought I, watching him drive off for town. And I would see the setting-up which was sometimes done in the half-dark of early morning before I was up. I would watch the engine weave its astonishing way up our country road guided by Eph while Bill sat high on the separator which would follow, drawn by heavy horses.

Placing the equipment exactly in line and at proper distances from (in the case of the separator) the mows and (of the engine) the buildings, which must not be exposed to sparks was, as my father put it, "a ticklish business."

"Jessie, you can help us," Mother said while she and my sisters flew about preparing a room for the threshers and starting at once to assemble ingredients for baking and cooking. By nightfall there would be crocks of smooth apple sauce from fruit which I had peeled. The cookie tins would be full and pastry mixed for the pies which would not be baked until morning; apple and elderberry pies, with flaky crusts, served just warm enough to delight the palate. There would be plates piled high with baking powder biscuits containing a scattering of currants. The biscuits would melt like snow when served with bowls of apple sauce, as a first dessert, to be followed, of course, by the waiting pies.

"I doubt if you'll get that roast into the oven, Frank," Mother said when he came home. "It's the biggest we've ever had."

"We'll get it in," he grinned. "It looked such an extra fine grain with the right amount of fat, I asked for a couple of pounds more than usual and Allison added another pound or so. It seems just right to me."

John Allison could be relied upon to offer the choicest beef to be found anywhere, my father said.

While I proceeded with the apple and potato peeling that afternoon, I sat on the veranda steps. I could smell the scent of pine roots burning and the sweet aroma of freshly cut straw carried on the wind that was blowing across our hollow from the O'Neil barn. Tomorrow night when the setting-up was being done and the firewood tried out, the air would be strong with dark smoke, instead.

I was usually allowed a tour of the barn while threshing operations were taking place, always with my father holding my hand, a promise which he made to Mother before I was permitted to go with him. He did very little but direct how certain things were to be arranged – where the new grain running from the drawer-like openings was to be placed, for instance, after it was lifted in the box-like container to make room for an empty one. "It's the belt I am always afraid of," Mother explained each year.

The belt ran in snapping revolutions between engine and separator, uniting the power with the machinery. Once, so Mother said, the small child of a neighbour had attempted to pass under the belt and had been struck and drawn into the waiting jaws beyond the sheaf carrier. The child had been horribly mangled. Neither my father nor I were likely to disobey Mother's warnings.

Sounds were as important as sights and scents on threshing day – the shrill blowing of the whistle which called the hands to attention, the threatening flap of the wide belt, the rattle of the carrier as it fed the sheaves, the swish of the sheaves themselves, and the soft drip of the pieces of stem and hull from the pipe onto the stack. As the men tossed the golden grain from mow to crawling carrier with gleaming forks, they exchanged orders and other information in loud voices, competing with the put-put of the engine and the grinding and groaning of the other machinery.

I loved threshing time – the sights and sounds, and the

105

coming of strangers to our table – cheery, off-handed and friendly, or silent and merely doing the bidding of their employers, one or two taking advantage of an audience which could not escape to voice their complaints and viewpoints about the government and the affairs of the community.

When the setting-up was completed, Eph and Bill came into the house and sat in the kitchen with my father. Mother and my sisters retired into The Room as soon as washing dishes and clearing away from supper was accomplished but I lingered beside my father. He drew me onto his knee. Once Mother had suggested that the place for a little girl of nine was not with strange men, but my father had observed that Eph and Bill were "decent spoken" and Mother had said no more. I noticed, however, that she left The Room door open and I judged that she and my sisters were also enjoying the conversation although taking no part in it.

The talk was usually of common enough things, but things which gave one a feeling of intimacy with the rest of the neighbourhood – a new barn erected, a thoroughbred horse that a stingy farmer had lost by underfeeding, the amazing size of crop achieved by another through the use of a new kind of fertilizer, the wife that bachelor-so-and-so had got himself through an advertisement in a city paper. All topics were mildly and leisurely discussed. I liked the drone of agreement and the tone of relaxation accompanied by an occasional yawn. I liked the chance to view Eph and Bill at close range without appearing ill-mannered, and of sharing my father's life.

When evening coolness settled in, my father occasionally added a stick to the low fire in the range, letting out a puff of smoke, the fragrance of which reminded me of burning leaves in autumn. Autumn was not far away.

Next morning I woke to the sound of the whistle blowing and the scent of pine smoke floating in at my open window. My sisters were already up and downstairs. The men had breakfasted and were in their places testing out equipment before the hands should arrive. I jumped from bed and quickly dressed. Mother scolded me for consuming my porridge at top speed but I must get to my favourite seat on the tongue of a wagon far enough from operations to be out of danger but near enough to participate.

Eph was in full view, tending the engine. He waved to me. I liked the brothers, but Eph was my favourite. Bill had lost a thumb at some time, and when I was in his presence I could not keep my eyes from resting on that chunky, huge hand, lacking so important a part. Being taught to ignore defects which had resulted in a deformity, I was constantly aware of guilt.

Eph's hands were long and rather slim for a man's. I heard him tell my father that he had wanted to be a musician; indeed, had played the violin for a while but couldn't afford lessons, also that his father had objected, declaring that he was wasting time. Eph's eyes had a dreamy look in them and he talked less than Bill. One year he brought me a book which had his name inscribed inside. It was titled *Freckles* by Gene Stratton Porter. He gave it to me rather unwillingly, I thought, as if parting from a loved friend.

"You like to read Jessie," he said. "Somebody give me this a while back. I read it twice and then some parts again. But I ain't got time for nonsense any more. When you grow up you won't have time either mebbe."

I loved the book which Eph gave me and never did I read it without thinking of him. As I grew older and understood better the nature of men, I sorrowed for Eph with his love of music and reading and his practical upbringing which had made earning a living with his hands the most important thing in life.

His voice was refined and gentle. Bill's voice was gruff and hard. Eph's movements were quick and agile; Bill's were lumbering and heavy.

I watched Eph as he reached up to blow the engine whistle. It emitted little shrieks and jets of white steam went up into the blue. The men hurried to their places. I had seen them cross the fields from north, south, east and west, each with a fork in his hand. The belt began to flap, and threshing had begun. The flapping sound changed to a deep hum as timing between engine and separator became almost perfect.

The threshers stayed a second night with us, that year, and they were not finished with my father's crop until mid-afternoon of the second day. They were served early dinner before travelling on to the next neighbour's. Later I could hear the hum of the machinery in an indentation near the southern ridge where the huge barns of our neighbour stood. I felt lonesome.

The second night Bill had gone to bed early, after ad-mitting tiredness. "He's too heavy," my father said to Eph who remained downstairs chatting. "He needs to take off some weight."

Eph smiled tolerantly. "He's always been like he is," Eph said. "When we were little fellows I used to beat him racing and playing ball because I could move faster, and for a while he tried to cut down on food but it was no use. He gave up ball playing rather than have to lose every time."

My father looked thoughtful. "A man won't take that kind of behaviour from an animal," he said quietly. "He lays on the whip and cuts down rations when he's in command. But he can't change it seems when it comes to bossing him-self. He'd rather indulge his appetite than win a race."

"Mebbe he needs more food than I do to keep up his strength," Eph said. "He works hard and he's never been like himself in spirit since Abbie died."

I began to listen more closely.

"Abbie was his wife?" from my father.

"No, it didn't get that far. They had the date set when she came down with some kind of fever, and Bill gave up work the last week or so and didn't leave her side. She died in his arms."

My father's arm was holding me. It tightened. When

Eph spoke again, it was gently. "He can't forget. He can't put anybody else where she was." My father nodded agreement. "Some are like that; you can't pity them, though," he commented, "because they know what love between a man and a woman can be."

"I got a good wife," Eph went on in a low voice. "She took after me when I was a young squirt and I guess she knew what she was doing. She didn't give up and she's not sorry, I hope. I love her, sure, but I never felt like Bill. She tells me that, sometimes. She knows, she's a woman." He laughed a little.

"They always do know even if they don't speak it out," my father answered. "Ma and I were sweethearts the first meeting and neither of us could see anybody else after. We've had our squabbles and sometimes things have been really hot, but we have never needed anybody's pity either. Every case is different."

"Sure, sure. I don't complain, mind you, but sometimes I get mad with her because she won't let me play the fiddle. I have one but I never touch it. The first year after we were married, we went to a shin-dig and I played for the folks because they asked me and when it came to going home, I wasn't ready, and she was, and that made the first trouble we ever had. I was good at dance music – *The Irish Washerwoman* and the *Highland Fling* and such as that. A girl was there from the city. She was small and pretty cute. She moved like a flash and when I played the *Fling*, she up and danced like a witch. Nobody could take their eyes off her. I was like every other fellow I suppose. Elsie was kind of fat and not too fond of dancing. She took time to look at me and what she saw didn't please her. She started for home by herself. It was a pitch black night, too. As soon as somebody told me she had went I stopped playing and made after her. I caught up to her the first quarter mile but she wouldn't have anything to say to me . . . cried and went on. I never played the fiddle anywhere after that, not even at home."

As I listened, I felt a great surge of emotion for Eph and I wanted nothing so much as to see him with a violin under his chin. In imagination I could hear his music. It would make me want to dance I felt sure. The light in the kitchen was dim but through the east window a rising moon fell full upon Eph's face giving it an ethereal look. The room was very still after his confession. I knew that my father sympathized with him and perhaps didn't know what to say. Far over the fields I could hear the gobble-gobble of Dan O'Neil's turkeys. Crickets were chirping and a tree toad sang in a mountain ash tree outside the window.

My brothers both played the violin, and Will, the inventive one, had made one for his own pleasure. Will was away now and had taken the instrument with him, but Al's hung in a green felt bag on The Room wall. Al was off shooting ground-hogs, that evening. He preferred hunting to playing, although he was fond of music, and had bought the instrument for himself.

I thought of a night during the previous summer when an old man with a long white beard and a slow walk had come up our hill at dusk. He had carried a battered case which turned out to contain a violin, too, but one without strings or a bow. He had once been a great musician we believed, who, now, scarcely knew who he was or had been. Mother prepared a cot in The Room for him to sleep on and gave him a warm meal. Al had offered his own violin to him but he had refused it. Then, during the night, we had been roused from sleep by the most beautiful music I had ever heard. Restrained by my father at the top of the stairs, we had listened until it had finished and the house was silent again.

In the morning, we found that the old musician had gone and Al's violin had been returned to its bag on the wall.

Impulsively I now slipped from my father's knee and went into The Room. Mother was mending there, bending intently over her work. Jean and Lill were occupied with cutting out a dress from a piece of cloth spread out on the bare dining table. No one looked at me.

I climbed onto a chair and took the felt bag from The Room wall. I tiptoed from The Room with it held against my breast.

When I gave the bag to Eph, I said, "Elsie isn't here, now."

He drew the instrument from its case and looked from me to my father. No one spoke, but there was a glistening softness in my father's eyes when I turned to him for approval. He drew me onto his knee very gently.

"Is it all right?" I whispered into his ear.

He held me close. "It's all right," he said gently. "Let's hear you play, Eph," he added, then.

Most of our men, like Bill, had gone to bed early. Others were away to the village store where many gathered at night. Eph hesitated, but my father said, "Bill won't hear you. He's at the other end of the house. He's probably snoring by now. Play, Eph." Then he added words which I wanted to hear. "Jessie can dance the *Highland Fling*, too. Can't you Jessie?"

I nodded proudly.

But it was not the *Highland Fling* which Eph played, that night. It was music soft and tender and touching to the heart. Piece after piece . . . it seemed to me that he would never stop playing. The house was listening. There was no other sound anywhere except the gobble-gobble of the turkeys and the accompaniment of the crickets and the tree toad. I could feel my father's heart beating a little faster, I thought, and now and then he put up his hand to wipe away a tear.

That was the most interesting threshing-time that I can remember.

Apple-Hat John

I was sorry for Apple-Hat John when he went up and down our road. At recess or during the noon hour when he passed by the school yard before reaching the village, a line of children gathered along the picket fence to stare at him. It was not what they knew about him but what they did not know which made Apple-Hat John so interesting. Sometimes a boy or girl who had not been trained to civility would call out rudely, "Hello, Apple-Hat. How's your stomach today?"

For it was common enough knowledge that John, whose surname was James, suffered from stomach trouble, caused, so the town doctor said, by eating too many apples and not enough of anything else.

Whatever the reason, Apple-John's body was lean to the point of bareness and his face was pinched. Wrinkles showed around the eyes and across the wide forehead. His unhappy look was what troubled me, for I was certain that he was unhappy.

I was one of those who watched him from the schoolyard and although I was not among those who called out to him, I was curious nevertheless. He was always in a hurry, always looked straight before him, and did not seem to hear the words which were shouted in disrespect.

He and Mrs. James were a middle-aged couple who lived several miles from the village. They were never known to ride anywhere. Their determination to stay young by walking was admirable, my father said, but there were times when Mother pitied Mrs. James, especially on rainy or stormy days when she did not carry an umbrella nor wear a raincoat, but walked smartly by her husband's side with eyes fixed upon the road, as were his.

113

Usually, however, when Apple-Hat John came to the village he came alone.

"I doubt if the poor woman gets beyond her own gate very often," Mother suspected. "I wonder sometimes what sort of life she has, although those who know her say that she never complains. Without young people or children in the home, it must be very dull."

"Perhaps she doesn't like children," my father said.

Mother was working the dasher churn in the pantry. She stopped and looked at him. "A woman always likes children," she said firmly.

She went on churning but listening for my father's reply: "You mean her man doesn't like them? I see you intend to blame Apple-John." His voice was amused.

I stood beside Mother, I thought she seemed to need my support.

"I'm not blaming anybody," Mother answered him. "But a woman was created to have children and love comes with the having, if she is normal. Liking is a mild kind of loving. Apple-Hat John doesn't look as if he liked anybody but himself."

"You forget," my father reminded her. "I guess almost everybody has forgotten. It happened so long ago."

"What has everybody forgotten?" I asked and he told me.

Before Apple-Hat and his wife came to live in our adjacent concession, one cold April day when the earth was scarcely rid of snow, a double phaeton had passed our gate. The phaeton had been part of a limited funeral procession and was preceded by a hearse marked by four black posts and drawn by two black horses.

"That was before your time," my father explained to me.

The Jameses had had a child, it seemed, a weakling from birth. He had died at seven years. Some said death was due to malnutrition caused by the parents' strange eating habits, but others declared that the boy had never been more than a skeleton and could neither walk nor talk.

"And yet," my father mused, "when John and his parents came from Ireland they were as fresh looking and sturdy as the Irish usually are. They took up land near father's farm. John was their only son but they had three daughters, all buxom and rosy-cheeked. None of them married, though, and they left home early. One was a dressmaker and lived from house to house. The other two went to the city, after they finished school, to work in a factory. They didn't come and go either, the way young folks do when there is good family feeling.

"I always felt sorry for Apple-Hat John," my father concluded. "He stayed at home with his folks until he was twenty-seven, then he married. He was quite the dandy when he was a young fellow, and smart spoken. He had a case on Belle for a while and never seemed the same after. She showed plain that she didn't care anything about him."

There were eight boys and two girls in my father's family. Belle or Isabella, named for a line reaching back centuries to the Queen of Spain, was the country's beauty. She was the eldest of the family – tall, dignified, with aristocratic carriage. Her dark hair and glowing dark eyes, my father claimed, had been inherited from a Spanish officer who had married into the family after being shipwrecked on Scottish shores.

"She was bossy, but men took off their hats to her," my father said. "She could have had the pick of them and she knew it, but she shrugged her shoulders until Jim appeared."

My uncle Jim was handsome and stately and also dark-eyed. They might have been brother and sister, my father reflected. "They made a fine-looking couple, and there was no question about the feeling between them. Jim seemed to enjoy Belle's bossiness. They got along like a pair of cooing doves."

115

It had been before Uncle Jim appeared that Apple-Hat John had come to call on Aunt Belle.

"His family had been wealthy in Ireland," my father said. "The father had owned a linen factory in Belfast and they set up farming in Canada in fine style. Everybody in the community was impressed – everybody but Belle that is. John always wore as good as Sunday clothes when he was at work in the fields and when he went to the village or into town he wore a fine outer coat and gloves, even in summer. He was looked up to by a lot of people but some laughed at him. He knew that. He couldn't take a joke, nor make one."

By the time my father had finished his description, I liked John James and pitied him. There followed the story of a memorable night when he had arrived at my grandfather's farm clad in a frock coat, white vest, and top hat. He had asked for Isabella.

Auntie Belle was in the kitchen helping Grandma to prepare the mixture for a haggis. It was between the New Year and Robert Burns' birthday, my father said. The latter was unfailingly celebrated by a traditional supper of which a genuine haggis was a part. One or two Scottish families, old friends of my grandparents, were invited. The dinner was followed by a program of songs, recitations and dances in which my sisters participated when they were very young women.

Lill had a voice like a bird, Jean's was soft and sweet. Dressed in costumes they sang the old ballads, *Caller Herrin* and *When Ye Gang Awa' Jamie*, while with the rest of those present, I listened with a lump in my throat. I could see the ship carrying Jamie away and Jeannie watching and weeping on the shore.

"Several of us boys were sitting along the wall behind the big kitchen range, the last time John visited us," my father related. "It was a cold winter's night and that was the warmest spot in the house. John James bowed very low to Belle with his hat in his hand. Then he placed the hat upside down on the corner of the table and sat down by the fire where father had set a chair for him. Father sat down, too, and they began to talk but John kept his eyes on Belle. Even though we were little fellows, we knew why he was there, and so did Belle. She came behind the stove to offer us apples from a dish, but really to speak to us.

" 'Don't any of you go to bed until I tell you,' she said in a stern whisper. She passed the apples to the visitor and to father. Then she went back to her haggis-making."

It was not their custom, as boys, my father said, to peel apples before eating them but that night was an exception. They had a purpose. They took out their pocket knives and set to work. There were three boys and three large apples. Murray, the youngest, was sitting at the end of the row next to the table where John James had placed his hat. The visitor sat facing the stove. He wasn't paying attention to any happenings in the room, my father said, except to what Aunt Belle was about. He gave random answers to Grandpa, showing that his mind was not on the conversation.

"Murray slipped along the floor on one hip," my father explained, "taking with him as many peelings as he could gather in his hands. He placed them quickly in the upturned hat and rejoined us. A few giggles did break out but a look from father silenced us. We became a little fearful of what was yet to happen but we need not have worried."

The rest of the evening passed quietly enough my father said.

Before John James left, Grandfather sent my father to the cellar for a basket of Northern Spies for the Jameses. John had remarked that although they had an apple orchard, it did not contain that variety.

"John James ate four apples that evening," my father chuckled, "and it was late before he got up to go home.

"We boys huddled down behind the stove when he picked up his hat. But being polite and mannerly he held it before him until he was outside the door. By then we were on our way to bed. Belle no longer needed us. Our mischief was never discovered until years later when we told Belle what we had done to discourage the beau she didn't care for.

" 'So that explained the strings of apple peelings I swept up on the outside door mat the next morning,' was all she said to us. Perhaps she considered herself to be as much to blame as we were."

I thought a great deal about Apple-Hat John after hearing this story. It had always been a puzzle to me how he got his name and now I knew.

I was glad when my father added a postscript, for I loved him and I felt a little ashamed of his boyish prank. "I tried to be friendly with Apple-Hat John," he said, "because he was really a decent fellow and he deserved better treatment. But the family moved away shortly after. I sometimes wonder if his queerness dated from the night we played our trick on him."

I hoped this was not so and I learned that it was not, a few weeks later when Mrs. James stopped by to purchase a setting of duck eggs from Mother. It was early spring and I was home from school with an attack of croup to which I was subject.

John James and Mrs. James parted at our gate, Apple-Hat going into the greenhouses east of the road where my father's figure could be seen through the glass. His wife came toward the house.

Mrs. James accepted Mother's invitation to come in rather gingerly, and to sit down even more gingerly, but once seated a minute she gave a sigh as if having accomplished a difficult task. She began to relax and to sip a cup of tea while Mother and she discussed the problems of duck-raising. I thought her quite pleasant. She was unattractively thin, it is true, so that her grey and white cotton dress hung on her without grace, but her face, though lean, had a wholesome healthy look. Her small dark eyes were clear and her dark hair parted in the centre and slicked down to a coil at

118

the neck, had a gloss to it. There was not any sign of greying.

"This is my girl Jessie," Mother said as I sat down on a stool near Mother.

Mrs. James did not look at me. She said, "I see," and sipped her tea as if she had known, and was not interested in me, and considered that Mother had wasted words. It seemed they were never wasted by Mrs. James.

Her call was short and without incident. She nodded and remarked, "I see," again when Mother outlined to her certain important points in setting duck eggs. The Jameses had not raised ducks before.

She looked startled and incredulous when Mother indicated unwillingness to take payment for the eggs.

"She acted as if I were being dishonest," Mother told my father later. "She seemed really annoyed with me," Mother said. "I didn't know what to do so I charged her the price that eggs are right now – hen eggs, I mean – and she seemed satisfied. Frank, it appears to me they must never have learned to give or to receive."

"You're right," he replied. "John admired the way my tomatoes are coming on. I offered him a small box with a dozen plants or so and he really acted offended. He said he and the wife didn't care much for tomatoes. That I doubt, but the man got quite talkative for him. He kept touching the side of his head near the temple with one hand. I asked him if he was troubled with headache. He said 'No' but that he got a crack on the forehead above the right eye when he was a boy. His father was raising the knife of a mower and he was standing too near. The handle hit him as it went up. He was knocked unconscious but soon came around. They didn't have a doctor, although the injury left him with poor eyesight, almost none on that side, and he still gets sharp jabs of pain in that part of his head. I suspect that lack of proper sight is why he looks straight before him and it's possible that the accident affected him other ways too."

I told my friend Tillie about Apple-Hat John's accident

the next time he and Mrs. James passed by the school yard.

"He looks in front of him because he has to," I said. "Nobody should make fun of him."

But Tillie looked at me with her big eyes and said in an uncompromising tone, "Mrs. James didn't get hit on the head," she reminded me. "She looks the same kind of way. What makes you so stupid, Jessie?"

And I had no answer to that.

The Fence Builders

Often during good weather, when my father drove to town, whether in our old buggy or in the easy-riding democrat, he took me with him if school were out. I preferred the old-fashioned buggy because one could sit in dignity partly concealed by the spars along the sides, pretending any number of things. One could imagine oneself a high born lady being driven through the park by a coachman for an airing on a summer afternoon, or a charity worker hastening to some place of concern to lend aid to the needy, or a haughty young woman caring nothing for anyone but herself, enjoying the privilege of being driven alone here or there, or just a happy child with her devoted father.

We had two buggies, the old and the new. The new was kept for church, for weddings and other times of importance; the old had a worn whipstock and one could see through the boards of the bottom thereby getting a sense of revolution by watching the movement forward over the sandy roadway. There were likewise two dusters – one a most conventional duster in brown and beige, patterned soberly and without fringe. The other was a light yellowish weave with a centre of roses and foxgloves in pink and blue respectively. It had a luxurious cream-coloured fringe and placing it over one's knee, was a matter of some pride. One could feel the expensive texture when smoothing it with the hand; I could never imagine myself a grand lady if the fringed duster were not in use.

I confided some of my thoughts about such matters to my father and he smiled tolerantly and nodded, indicating that he heard me and was not disgustingly amused as some grown ups are when children express their special kind of thoughts. Yes, my father was a great comfort to me.

The road to town wound from the village by a mounting woodland on one side where, in spring, the bank showing between the trees was a riot of wild flowers; on the other the river flats lay grassy and moist. This short stretch of boggy land was flowered with wild iris and marsh-marigolds in abundance. Frogs croaked in blue pools. Beyond the flat land was the winding Grand river, beautiful in sun or shade, with cattle roaming beside it and through to the opposite bank. Tall elms and cedars graced the flats and gave shelter to countless birds. Below were water birds, ducks, herons, cranes, with plenty of sand pipers and red-winged black-birds, sometimes a teetering kingfisher above the water's edge on a tilting bough. In the trees gathered the songsters from the land, well hidden, and with water close by if they desired to bathe or to drink.

Over all stretched the sky, often billowy, sometimes a friendly grey when rain was pending.

The road had many twists and turns and one was pre-pared for surprises, such as a swiftly driven vehicle coming the other way, or a heavily loaded wagon with creaking wheels and powerful horses, or someone on foot, always of interest because those were the days of wayfarers and persons in search of work from many parts of the world. It was common enough for a driver to stop and pass the time of day with such persons, perhaps giving them a chance to tell their story and their purpose.

Once we had met a wanderer from the circus in town with a monkey sitting on his shoulder, the monkey tethered by a chain. Once, an old woman leading a child by the hand. She had been travelling with the child and a small boy of ten. They were waiting at the town railway station for a required change of train when the boy disappeared along the stretch-ing roadway and the woman followed in the hope of finding him. My father explained that we had not seen him and offered her a ride back to town and the promise of police assistance, but as we passed through the railway abutment

123

just at the entrance to the residential area, there lay her son, asleep in the grass of the roadside. It was a happy moment. He clambered into the democrat and thankfully returned to the depot with his mother and sister, where a train was puffing in preparation for leaving.

"Father, oh Father . . . listen to the frogs. Please listen," I would say on a balmy April day when the sun was high and the sky blue. The pools were many in the soaking fields. My father would bring the horse to a halt and respectfully listen with me, neither of us uttering a sound to detract from the natural music of spring-time which always held me spellbound.

And there was autumn when the thorn apple trees began to shed their abundance onto the drying grass. The tiny apples were rosy and tempting until one bit into their stony centre, but the flavour was rare and also the fragrance. My father would help me to alight over the great wheel and wait until I had filled the pockets of my dress or perhaps gathered as many as I could into a little crocheted bag which Jean had made in purse-like style for me. Then, blithely, we would journey on, he refusing a share in the fruit which had such an allurement for me.

Snake fences followed the line of the fields and woods along one side and part of the other; but when we neared the town, the gray rails disappeared, and a well-built structure of stones fitted together took their place. Fences of stone led on for about a mile on both sides of the road.

My father waved his whip as we passed a field in which a man was at work placing the stones, with a young boy helping him. Behind them in the centre of a pasture of clover was a strange-looking house built on wheels. A wagon tongue lay forward between the wheels and one day as we passed by, the man and the boy were enacting the part of horses as they pulled the house to a shady nook under the trees, for the day was excessively hot.

My father explained to me, then, that the father and son

were from a country where stone fences and dykes were common. They had a skill in building which Canadians do not have, he said, and were much in demand by farmers who could afford this special kind of fence. It astonished one to learn that the slabs of stone were in no way attached to each other but so piled on and against each other that they remained in place without masonry.

The man and the boy were both tall and very thin, with faces and hands tanned almost to copper colour by daily exposure to the weather. They worked industriously and did not pay any attention to the traffic on the road. "Some day," my father said, "when we have time, we'll tie up and go in for a visit. But I'm not sure that they can speak English well enough to carry on a conversation with us."

"Doesn't the boy go to school?" I asked.

"I think he must be past the age, he's quite a big fellow," my father said. "No doubt he's getting a kind of education that lots of boys would appreciate – out here in the open air and busy at work he seems to enjoy."

I looked for the pair each time we passed along the road and until the autumn days grew bitterly cold, they were always there.

I should have liked to wave my hand to the hard-working boy but I was shy at any time, and inclined to be over-proper in my behaviour. I did not wave.

Nearer town, we often met a woman walking alone. She was plainly dressed and her face was reddened by exposure; the skin had a leathery appearance. She, too, did not look at us, but kept to the side of the road and always seemed as if looking for something lost.

"Is she going to meet somebody?" I asked one day.

"It's a sad case," my father said, "and I'll tell you about it, Jessie, now that you ask me. It must be five or more years ago that she was married to a fine young fellow and they came here on their honeymoon to visit relatives. He went out shooting one morning early. It was very hot, and they think that he decided to take a dip in a small lake not far off that has a mud bottom. She walked a mile or so out of town with him and that's how far she walks now, looking for him every day of her life.

"They found his loaded rifle lying in the rushes beside the water. His body was never found though, and she wouldn't believe that he had died. She has never believed it. They loved each other very much, you see, and that makes people like one person, it's as if part of her was missing and she is looking for that part. Her folks have tried and tried to convince her of what happened but it's no use, she still looks and waits for him."

I felt my heart throb with sorrow as I listened to this story and I have never passed along the road since that day without thinking of the woman whose lover meant so much to her.

The day that my father had time to stop for a talk with the fence builder, the man was working by himself; in broken English he explained to us that his son was ill. He led us to the one-roomed house set under a tree. Although the shade was protecting it, the heat of an intensely warm summer day was almost unbearable where it stood. Inside was a home-made wooden bed divided up the middle by a space about a foot wide. On this bed lay the boy panting for breath; he had been soaked by a drenching rain while at work a few days before, his father said, but had worked on. A brisk wind had come up and his clothing had dried on him. In the morning he had complained of a pain under his shoulder on the right side and now for two days he had been suffering with every breath. Under the tan of his skin, there was a redness which even I recognized as a sign of fever.

"You should have a doctor," my father advised, touching the boy's forehead. "He's burning up and it's not the heat of the day."

"We get well without doctor in our country," the man said rather firmly.

My father shook his head. "That may be," he reasoned, "and some get well here without, too. But there are times when that doesn't happen and I'm afraid this is one of the times. My wife and I have a family and we have a doctor who is a splendid fellow. This is our youngest girl and she has been sickly, she wouldn't be alive today if we had tried to manage by ourselves. This doctor lives in town. We are going in, now, for some supplies and if I tell him about your boy, he will come out and see him. He's too sick to be moved, I think."

Now the man shook his head. "We get well without doctor in our country," he repeated.

"There's not much one can do when a man refuses to be convinced," my father said to me as we drove on. "I wish Ma had come with us, today. She isn't as blunt as I am. She gets around people better."

As we were leaving the town for home about five o'clock, after picking up a supply of groceries and a bridle that was being repaired at the harness shop, we met the doctor coming back from a country call. The sorrel mare was wet with sweat and the doctor looked tired and half asleep on the buggy seat, but he knew us and stopped.

My father told him about the sick boy.

"A man who is stubborn should never marry," the doctor said grimly, "too many have to suffer because of the pig-headedness of one. There's nothing worse than being too sure you're right. I'm on my way to a confinement case, now, but if everything goes well I should be free in an hour or two. I'll take a look at the boy. I noticed the man in the field and I know where to find them."

But everything did not go right, we learned a day later. The doctor sat with his patient far into that night. It was morning when he reached home again, and another emergency was waiting.

In the meantime my father had told Mother about the boy in the strange little house. "There's no question about it," he said, "he's burning up with fever, I've half a mind to

127

drive back in the morning just in case the doctor didn't get to him or that, if he did, the father wouldn't have anything to do with him."

"I'll go with you as soon as the men have breakfast," Mother told him. "I'll take along what I think would help – mustard for a poultice, and some honey and lemon like I give Jessie when she has a cough. Is there any water nearby?"

"A stream below the slope of the field."

"I'll take towels. He may need a sponge to bring down the fever. Lill, pack up a basket with a bowl of that custard we had for supper, last night, and make a bottle of lemonade. Put in a couple of scones and a jar of black currant to sweeten up the father."

Lill laughed. "She knows how to win favour," she said.

"She needs to know in this case," my father muttered. "I put a tub in the back of the democrat for a hot foot bath. They must surely have some way of heating water; but in case they haven't, set the kettle full in the corner and plug the spout with a cloth. It's hot but not boiling. It won't burn you. How about the goose grease, Ma?"

"Oh, yes, and the flannel tail of your old winter shirt. Vaseline, too, to rub on after the mustard."

Mother was mixing the mustard with flour and pouring it into a paper bag.

I did not go with my parents on their errand of mercy. I went to school for it was the end of August and school had reopened, but I could think of nothing but the sick boy. I gathered a knot of children about me in the school yard and told them of him. Everyone was interested and excited.

Tillie sat behind me in the classroom. After school was called, following recess, I tried to keep my mind on my work but instead I found myself plotting a story about the boy in the wagon house. I had grown up and was now a nurse in a starched white uniform. I had finished my training and was engaged by our doctor to attend his patients. . . . Under my care the boy began to recover, and what could have been

128

more natural than that he should have changed into a young man with whom I fell in love? For me imagining was a delightful pastime and thus engaged I lost my concern for the welfare of the actual. When the teacher called for the results of a geography lesson which had included the drawing of a map of Ontario on which rivers were to be outlined, I had not placed a single river but the Grand, which flowed along in the valley beside the field where the boy lay.

I was reprimanded, and Tillie managed to whisper to me without being heard. "I know why you didn't get your work finished," she said a little scornfully. "You were thinking about that boy. You're really glad he's sick aren't you? You ought to be ashamed."

I was ashamed. In fact, I was so ashamed that a tear or two fell on my work book. How could I be such a cruel person? How could I? I had made a story out of the unhappiness of another and in doing so I had been happy. I felt crushed by Tillie's straightforward analysis of me, her best friend. I bent over my reader which was open at our next reading lesson and tried to understand myself. The poem to be studied was also the story of suffering, and it was my favourite in the book.

Into a ward of the whitewashed walls
Where the dead and the dying lay—
Wounded by bayonets, shells, and balls—
Somebody's darling was borne one day.
Somebody's darling! so young and so brave . . . *

When called upon to read, I hung my head. My voice was unsteady, and faint.

"Sit down, Jessie," said the teacher.

I sat down thankfully. I found my handkerchief and bent under the desk to use it.

I felt a touch on my back. I raised up and listened to Tillie whispering again, but this time in a soft, kind voice. "I'm a mean pig," Tillie said. "After school I'll walk home

*Marie Ravenal de Lacoste

with you and find out about that boy from your mother. She's back; I saw the democrat go up the hill while you were blubbering. Stop crying, Jessie."

Tillie walked home with me.

The news was good. Mother and the doctor had both done their work and the boy was much better.

But I was not happy until I had said my prayers, that night, until I had asked forgiveness for the pleasures of an ungovernable imagination.

The stone-fence builders moved into a small house near town for the winter. Work was at a standstill then on the land but the father took what he could find to do as a day labourer and the boy ran errands for our butcher, John Allison.

Early in December, the father came walking through the snow to tell us that his wife was arriving from Europe in time for Christmas. His weather-beaten cheeks were wet with tears as he told us that she would bring their small daughter with her and that, now, after three years' separation, the family would be together again.

On Christmas morning a light sleigh was the first vehicle to mark the new fall of snow on our road. The man and the boy were on the seat of the sleigh and bundled in blankets on the floor behind them were a woman and a little girl.

When the sleigh stopped at our gate, we were all prepared to welcome the strangers, and Mother hurried to put on a kettle and to set out currant bread and cheese, a favourite combination with us at Christmas time.

But only the boy came in. He carried a box wrapped in white paper which he gave to Mother. "We wish Merry Christmas to you everybody that we like great deal," he said in a hearty voice and before Mother could say a word of thanks in reply, he was gone.

My father, coming from chores at the barn, was able to reach the sleigh before it drove off. The rest of us watched from the window as he shook hands with the parents, gave the boy a pat on the shoulder, and tucked the wool blanket more closely around the little sister.

As they drove off, the boy looked back at the window and this time I waved my hand.

The box which the boy gave to Mother contained a variety of dried and sugared fruits such as I had never seen.

"Even stubborn people can be convinced if you go about it the right way," my father observed as he bit into a plump fig. "You did a fine job, Ma."

Mother was examining a sugared date. She turned to my father with the date half way to her mouth. "We're all pretty much alike, I think," she said simply. "Giving in isn't easy for anybody. Some take longer to be convinced than others. The pity of it is that delay is sometimes so dangerous."

He nodded. "Not more dangerous than snap judgment," he reflected. "Either way man's a pretty foolish being if he thinks too much of his own opinion."

CHAPTER
14

Angus of the Red Muffler

"I wonder who the man with the red muffler is," Mother said one summer day. "This is the fourth time I have seen him going by in the past week, and although the weather is warm, he always has his throat covered. Perhaps he isn't well."

My father was reading the *Family Herald and Weekly Star*. He was sitting by the east window of the kitchen. Supper was over and Mother was putting the food away while my sisters did the dishes. I was reading *Grimms' Fairy Tales* for the fifth time.

"His name is Angus," my father said. "I found out at the mill today. He came in while I was there and Joe introduced us. I forget the last name."

Joe was the miller and knew everyone in the countryside.

"Angus" Mother mused. "That's a nice name isn't it? I wish you could remember the surname, though, then we'd have some idea of his nationality. Where does he come from and what does he do, I wonder?"

"He's a Scot whatever his surname is. He has bought a piece of grazing land from Watson's," my father said. "It seems his people were shepherds in Scotland. He's a sheep-keeper. Very fond of the animals, Joe says, and the story goes that he never loses a ewe or lamb in lambing time. He has a gentle way with him and a mild voice. I took to him at once. He's about thirty, Joe thinks. Not married I believe, lives by himself in the small house he bought with the land. Keeps it as tidy as a woman could, Joe says. Joe accepted an invitation to visit him and see his flock a week ago. Says he hardly ever comes to the village unless he needs supplies; he has a lot of shelves full of books and spends his free time reading. Joe thinks he has been a scholar and for some reason drawn away from people."

133

In time we learned more about Angus of the Red Muffler, and that his surname was Ellis.

We owned a flock of sheep, also, and my brother Al was shareholder of them with my father. He was about five years younger than Angus but they had mutual interests and became fast friends. Al supervised the tilling of that part of our land which was given over to farming, and during haying and harvest Angus took work by the day with us. His own land did not require full-time attention.

Often, instead of going home immediately after the evening meal, and chores were done, Angus would stay for a chat with my father and brother. Our veranda was wide and ran around two sides of the house. It was the favourite place of our men for visiting. The warmth of summer often kept me out of doors, too, until bedtime, and in that way I heard conversations which helped me to understand the nature of those who were strangers within our gates. Where my father was, discussion was always civil and restrained, but even so, when I was present, Mother hovered in the background, always alert.

There were a few times when Angus and my brother stood alone in conversation under the big elm tree by the side of the lawn, or stretched themselves on the grass below, speaking in quiet tones. When I would have joined them, Mother called me into the house.

Then one early evening in autumn, the second year that Angus lived in our community, the time of turnip pulling and potato digging, Angus went home before supper and Al came smiling in to tell us why.

"He told me a while ago that he had a wife and little girl but his wife didn't want to come out into the country until he was settled for certain and getting along," Al explained. "They are staying with a relative in Toronto. He's making a go of it, now, and this summer he's been getting furniture together. You should see what he's done. Good stoves and comfortable beds. He needs a little help with curtains and things before she gets here. She's coming on Monday. I told him you'd be glad to give a hand, Ma."

It was Thursday evening.

My sisters were eager to help too. "If you would drive them out to see the place they would measure the windows," Mother said. "And I have plenty of curtaining on hand that I'll never use for us. We can run up something pretty in a short time and maybe add a few touches that will please the girl."

"She isn't exactly a girl," Al smiled. "She is two years older than Angus."

"Two years isn't much," Mother said. "Some times it's a good way for the difference to be. I'm so glad he'll have company for the winter and the house isn't far from the corner schoolhouse. I suppose the child is old enough to go."

"Jessie's age," Al said.

I was ten then.

"They couldn't have been married too early; the mother is probably a nervous type. I don't think Angus would choose anybody who wasn't sensible, though.

"Not likely," my father, who was listening, answered.

Al said nothing.

Mrs. Ellis, who had been a city girl, was small, pretty, and dressed stylishly. She spoke very little when Angus brought her to call and to thank us.

"She's not sure of herself, yet. Kind of strange," my father commented after. "I asked her if she enjoyed country life and she said she thought she would, and knew that she would be happy."

"That has the right sound," Mother said. "She doesn't say much and I felt kind of anxious."

But it was Cora who delighted me. She was blonde and doll-like in appearance and as merry as an elf. We got along together very well although I felt heavy and stupid beside her. I moved slowly and spoke slowly, she moved quickly and spoke quickly, like her father. Angus was a small slight man, boy-like and blonde, too.

The Ellises did not come often and I saw much less of Cora than I wished but we sent messages to each other, and when Christmas arrived Angus brought his family to have dinner with us, and they went with us to the Sunday School entertainment that evening.

The entertainment was for all ages and included a two-act play produced by the adult young people. This was the last number on the programme. Until then everyone seemed to be enjoying themselves very much. The Ellises attended a Sunday School in the concession on the south of us and therefore Cora had no part in the Snow Pageant which was presented by our Sunday School class, but one had only to look at her face and the faces of her parents to know that they appreciated what was done and were glad to be there.

The play was announced as, *Murder Will Out*. Of course we were excited by the name because it suggested mystery and intrigue. Usually plays produced by the grown-ups of the Sunday School were horribly dull.

"I bet somebody gets killed or something," Tillie giggled. She sat on one side of me and Cora on the other.

"Is that what it's about?" Cora whispered.

"I don't know, but I think so," I confided happily.

Cora looked troubled. "My mother won't let me read murder stories," she said. "Maybe she'll take me home."

Evidently Mrs. Ellis was like the very religious people who didn't believe in hearing about the wicked part of life, I thought. If this had been true of Angus Ellis, I could have understood because he was so gentle and kind, but Cora's mother had a more worldly look; I thought of her as the heroine in an exciting kind of story.

But Mrs. Ellis, when I looked back to where she was sitting beside Mother, was smiling and enjoying herself. "I don't think she will take you home," I said to Cora.

The play began with two young men plotting a robbery.

Both had good reason, they thought. One had been born poor, and his only child was a cripple and needed an expensive operation. He had appealed to friends, including the minister of his church, but no one had come through with assistance. The other young man was a ne'er-do-well in the community, whose father had died when he was a small child, and whose mother had had a struggle to bring up three children.

Neighbours tried to persuade her that it was her duty to place the children in an orphanage or marry again, but she had resolutely continued to work to provide for them and when the young man in question became old enough to enjoy life, he had little with which to enjoy it. He became restless and chose unfortunate companions. The play was built upon the moral that honesty is the best policy even if one must starve, and that the improper choice of companions leads to an ill fate.

The second scene showed the two young men in possession of a satisfactory amount of this world's goods, living well and their crime undiscovered. Then followed the exciting and convincing part of the lesson. The cripple had gained the needed surgical attention but died during the operation. The young man who now had money with which to enjoy life was constantly haunted by a sense of guilt and could find no enjoyment. He had dropped an initialled handkerchief during the robbery, and lived in constant fear of being identified as the killer of a policeman who had been murdered the same night close to the place where the robbery had occurred. Although the two young men had been innocent of this murder, in the last part of the play they were taken into custody to be tried for an act which they had not committed.

The play showed some originality in ending on this unfinished note, and the impression left upon young minds was perhaps more lasting because of it. What had really happened to the young men? Had they indeed been found guilty of the murder? The shock of this possibility was a deterrent to un-lawful behaviour.

It was a beautiful starlit winter's night when we emerged from the school building where the entertainment had been held. The fields lay white with snow and the ridge along the west was purple black with pines above which hung a falling moon. Far off we heard a dog barking and another answering. Lights twinkled in windows and the trail of the road before us was sponged here and there with a soft glow where a house stood close enough for its light to fall upon the wheel-way.

The Ellis family walked on when our gate was reached, although Mother invited them in for a cup of tea with scones and currant jam, which was always the ending to entertainment night at our house. My sisters had hurried home before us to prepare the simple repast.

"Do you think they enjoyed themselves?" Mother asked my father as we turned in the lane.

"Oh, I think so," he replied. "Although I can't say I liked the dialogue at the end. It didn't make sense. Didn't tell the whole story."

"That's what I mean." Mother continued. "I looked at Mrs. Ellis when the last part was half over and her face was white and I thought she was going to cry. Did you notice him at all?"

"I didn't," my father said. "I was thinking about Robbie Martin. He was there. You remember he was mixed up in some sort of crooked work last year and had to pay a fine? Was friends with a boy in the grocery store in town who had access to the till and helped himself, sharing with Robbie, I suppose, for Robbie was involved too. Maybe the play was a lesson, and maybe it was a kind of cruel reminder. I didn't like it anyway."

A week later, when Yuletide festivities were still at their height, Angus Ellis appeared in the stable of our barn when my father was mixing the cow feed ready for the evening meal.

This the men would distribute in measured proportions according to the requirements of the cattle now stabled.

"I think all of us as a family ought to know this," my father said, later that night, when supper was over and Angus had gone home without accepting an invitation to partake of it with us.

Mother, my sisters, and I were gathered with him in The Room. The coal fire was sending spouts of red and blue flame upward behind the mica and the wind was wailing in the chimney. It was a stormy night and Angus had given my father this as an excuse for going home before darkness settled in closely.

"Al isn't here," I said. What we were all to know I could not guess, but my brother was absent and should be included I thought.

"Al knows about it," my father said. "He has known for a long time, I guess, but didn't mention it even to me – I respect him for keeping the confidence of another. Angus told him everything shortly after he moved to the farm, and I see now that is why Al has been such a friend to him – trying to help as best he could."

"Whatever is the matter, Frank?" from Mother while my sisters leaned forward in their chairs, and I scarcely breathed as I sat on a cushion by my father's feet.

"Angus is in trouble," he said. "Al will feel bad when he hears the news. His wife left him, today, and went back to her relatives in the city. She took the child with her. She gave as an excuse that she is going to have another and needed medical care, but it appears that Angus has been taking her regularly to the doctor in town and knows that this isn't the real reason." My father turned to me. "You're getting to be a big girl, Jessie," he said seriously. "That's why I am letting you hear what I have to say. I know you can be trusted not to mention it to anyone."

I was crying. "Did she take Cora away?" I sobbed.

"Why did she do such a mean thing?"

"She didn't intend to be mean," he explained. "She just didn't realize what a cruel thing she was doing, especially to Angus. He is a sicker man than she is a woman, and needs her, but sometimes the people who think they are doing right are more sinful in the sight of God than those called sinners. When Cora was a baby her father was drunk one night and got mixed up in a brawl with men on the street as he was coming home very late. One of the men was a prize fighter who had been drinking too and he hit one of the other fellows, knocking him down; the fellow struck his head on the pavement.

"A policeman was coming around the corner and saw the man fall, but didn't see who hit him. The prize fighter swore Angus had done it. The man died and there was a trial. Angus was found guilty and was sent to a gaol for ten years. He got out before the time was up for good behaviour, but only on parole which means somebody checks up on him every so often. Angus thought the checking-up time was over when he moved to the farm, and hadn't been reporting to his parole officer for several months, but there had been a mistake on the papers from the court and he was still expected to go. I guess they didn't notice for a while and then couldn't find him but yesterday an officer came looking for him. He stopped in the village to ask the way, and told why he was looking for Angus.

"It was a contemptible thing to do. There should be a penalty for such things. Angus has never touched liquor since he got out of gaol and he told Al that he never will again. He is what they call an alcoholic which is a kind of disease. His wife knew and should have trusted him; he hasn't broken his promise a single time. He told me everything. I'm going to intercede with the authorities for him. He's a good honest man, and a valuable asset to any community; he wouldn't willingly hurt anyone. He hasn't it in him. How the woman could leave him, I don't know. It's cut him to the heart and

140

I'm afraid for him. I wish Al was home." Al had gone to Guelph to visit cousins for a few days, since work on the farm was slack. "Al is nearer his age. I asked Angus to stay the night here but he has a sick sheep and said he must get back to give it a warm feed."

As a family, we sat long, thinking. Viewpoints were exchanged about what had happened.

"The young man needs a woman's sympathy right now," Mother said. "It's a woman he has lost you know. When morning comes we'll take the cutter and go to see him, Frank. I'll maybe find out how to get in touch with the wife; she surely can't be in her right mind to leave him at this time, unless she *is* sick, but even then she must love herself more than she loves him. The more a person needs loving," Mother went on, looking at me as if teaching a lesson, "the more love we should give to them."

I went to bed sorrowing. I knelt to pray for everyone concerned but especially for Cora. I had lost a friend but she had lost a father. Surely no loss could be more terrible than that. Perhaps she would come running back to him the way I would come running if anyone took me away from my father.

I woke very early and got softly out of bed to look from the window. It was still dark but the rose light of morning was beginning to touch the east. The road looked purple in the morning darkness and my eyes were strained to see if I could distinguish anyone travelling there. Oh, if only Cora would have the courage. Then I did see someone; it was the figure of a man hurrying through the heavy snow toward the bend in the road leading to the village.

His figure was indistinct but I could identify it. It was Angus. I heard my father going down the stairs. He always rose early and with Al away would help the men with the chores. I ran down after him. I told him what I had seen.

He was lighting the lantern preparatory to going to the barn. There was no other light in the kitchen but I could see his face clearly enough to realize that he was troubled; then

141

his look brightened. "No doubt he's off to the city to see if he can't get his family home. Don't worry, Jessie. It's probably the wisest thing that he could do. Now run back to bed."

The day passed and the night and another day came. My father made a trip to town by cutter and spoke stern words to the Department of Justice there, but though they promised to reprimand the officer, the mischief had been done.

The second day, Al came home. When he heard the news, he and my father rode off in the light sleigh to see if Angus was back. But he had not returned and the sheep had extra feed and water in their pens.

"We put enough in for another day," my father said. "He thinks too much of his stock to leave them uncared for. He'll be home soon, for sure."

About noon, a slick-looking horse and cutter came swiftly up our road. A man tethered the horse to our hitching post and came to the door. He asked for my father and Mother directed him to the greenhouses where my father was transplanting that day.

After a half-hour or so, the man drove away and my father came slowly to the house.

Between our village and the nearest town was a railway by means of which those without vehicles could travel to and fro – buggies and wagons were, however, the common means of transportation. There were two trains each day, one in the morning, and one in the late afternoon. In the blur of a snowstorm that morning the engineer had not seen the figure lying prone upon the track, not until he became aware of something impeding the speed of the locomotive as the cowcatcher lifted and bore the body of a man forward with it.

In an attempt to drown his sorrow and his heartbreak, and perhaps fears, my father said, Angus had turned to find help from his greatest enemy. He had tried to return after being ordered from the public house where he had spent a day and late into the night drinking. He had chosen the dark rails of the track as a guide toward the village, for the new heavy fall of snow had obliterated the roadway. In a drunken stupor he had pitched forward, and been dragged to his death.

No one ever found out where his wife and daughter had gone, not even the investigator responsible for the tragedy. Cora became only a sad memory. But in after years I sometimes made my way up the long hill to the small village cemetery where we buried Angus, and I stood looking in grief at the modest stone which my brother, Al, sorrowing for a good friend, had had erected to his memory.

ANGUS ELLIS

Aged thirty years

There was a third line chiselled into the granite, grown over by the dark moss which attacks memorials with the passing of years:

He fought a good fight.

The spring freshets had started to run. Blue rivulets forced their way through the clay-coloured mud of the road and between the small grain furrows of the fields. The river itself was well up its banks and had a rollicking appearance as if enjoying the first freedom from the ice and snow which had restrained it all winter long.

It was the beginning of April and the earth was showing green. There was, however, a sharp sting to the wind still, and it remained high. Although crocuses were out and wild flowers beginning to bud, the fear of frosts remained and the farmers looked upon their awakening wheat fields and their budding orchards with some concern.

In a hollow near our swamp a half-dozen wild ducks settled and remained for several days. Standing at the gap from the last pasture field before the swamp began, I could smell the reviving growth of cedar and pine, and the rich wildness of swamp grasses and rushes.

The sky was bright blue with an abundance of white clouds scudding before the wind. When the sun set, that night, it would flame more like a winter sunset than one associated with spring. Winter was not quite out of the door, as was indicated also by a biting wind.

That winter there had been extra to do in the house, because my brother Will was to be married the following summer, and preparations were well under way. "He must have at least six quilts and comforters," Mother said, "and you girls should start making pretty things to go with them."

Mother had always claimed that when a man married, his bride should not be expected to do all the preparing – that his family should help her in every way.

"If we didn't have so many cows to milk," Mother complained to my father.

We had ten that winter and my sisters helped with the milking. Mother churned the cream and prepared the butter for sale in pretty pound-sized bricks with a decorative top – a bunch of grapes on a stem.

"How be we get a hired girl for a spell?" my father suggested. "Then Jean and Lill can help you sew carpet rags and quilt, and the girl can help with the meals and the milking and what not."

It was in this way that Lulu came to our house. She had been employed on a neighbour's farm for the past year but the neighbour now had two half-grown girls who could be pressed into service after school hours, and felt that he did not need other help.

Lulu was a veritable dumpling. She had a pretty face and large blue eyes and straight blonde hair which was never tidy. Yet she gave the appearance of cleanliness and was indeed very clean about her person. But she bulged in all directions; her bust was so pronounced that I tried not to look at it. Her hands were small as were her feet, but legs and arms puffed out to ankles and wrists. Her face was round with a pasty look – her lips were full and red.

Lulu was attractive to men. This was proved when she told my father, upon hiring, that she would not be able to remain with us more than the rest of the year, because she would be married in the coming January. Her husband-to-be was a seasonal worker whose reputation was that of unreliability and a tendency to roam. Lulu and he would be opposites indeed. She seemed content to move as little as possible, and lacked the imagination which roaming people usually display.

We were fond of Lulu and she became almost one of the family. As well as making things for my brother's wedding, Mother was active in preparing for Lulu's and the quilting which might have stopped with autumn went on through the fall season until Christmas. Lulu had lost her parents in early life and had no sisters. Her large blue eyes were tearful with appreciation as she looked upon the donations to her dowry and to her wardrobe.

About three weeks before the wedding, Lulu left us to stay with a family twenty miles away, who had offered to have the wedding performed in their home. My sisters lacked the appreciation of Lulu which my mother had, and although we were all invited to the wedding, it was decided that only Mother and my father would go, taking me with them.

I had attended my brother's wedding which had whetted my appetite for more such excitement. His bride had not been well known to us and they went to live in the city where he was following an engineering career. She was pretty and intelligent but a withdrawn type of young woman, therefore my participation in the wedding had been little more than that of any other guest. With Lulu it would be different, I felt sure; she hugged me warmly when saying good-bye and reminded me that I was to be her "little maid-of-honour."

Jean made a fluffy white dress for me and the frills of lace and the ribbon bows satisfied my liking for decorative clothing. My hair, which was curly, was to be arranged in a tie-back fashion with a rich, blue satin ribbon which matched the bows on the dress.

We hoped for a mild winter's day for the wedding but in truth the temperature was colder than was usual for that time of the year and a snowstorm threatened. We set off in the cutter about two o'clock in the afternoon with a long sack of warm grain at our feet and plentiful robes. Glints of sunshine pierced the clouds and touched the snow-capped hills with sparkling gold, and now and then a whiff of snow would be blown over us by a light gust of wind. The sky had a threatening look, and my father said he hoped we were not in for a storm, at least until we reached home again which would probably be very, very late, perhaps even close to morning. For it would take us three hours of driving to reach the farm where Lulu was waiting.

The wedding was set for five-thirty and after that there

147

would be the wedding supper, "and all sorts of high jinks" as my father put it, including a dance which he looked forward to with much pleasure. Mother was fond of dancing, also, but he had been the prize waltzer of his community when a young man, although he couldn't carry a tune, Mother said, in spite of his perfect sense of rhythm.

"I have seen the time," he admitted, "when I danced every night of the week and worked hard all day as well. Once when Friday came, I remember listening to the fiddles at our neighbour's across the fields and knowing that I hadn't enough strength left to go. How I regretted this, for I enjoyed the amusement more than any other!"

When we reached the home where Lulu was to be wed, I was whisked upstairs to her room at once and my wraps removed. Lulu, dressed in a flowing robe of white taffeta with a confining bust and waist-line, and with her hair piled high, was a lovely creature. She welcomed me with a hug and praised my costume which she said was "just right" as she knew it would be "if your sister Jean made it." Although Jean had kept aloof from Lulu a little, being offended by her untidiness, perhaps, or her undisciplined manners, Lulu had often remarked, "Jean, you are a swell girl. You ought to get married to a real fine guy."

It was years later before Mother told me the whole story of Lulu's romantic experiences. This, it seemed, was not her first preparation for marriage. There had been a time, two years before, when she had gone about becoming a bride with even more happiness. She had been living in the north country then with a French Canadian woodsman and his family. There she had met a cousin of the family, a man somewhat older than herself who had not been married before and who showed her great attention, finally asking her to be his wife.

"He was a shy fellow," Mother said, "according to reports, and had always kept clear of women, that is in a serious way. Well, it seems that after he and Lulu were

148

engaged, she was very eager about marrying. He began to cool off, then, and about a week before the wedding was to take place he went to the nearest town to buy himself a suit, so he told her. He never came back."

Lulu, dressed and waiting, would not believe that he had deserted her, Mother said, until two days had passed. The minister had come and gone and the guests had departed, but Lulu remained clad in her wedding dress expecting him to arrive, and announced to everyone that they would then drive to the home of the minister and be quietly married there. Finally, she disrobed; and dressed in warm outside attire, she set off on foot for the town, certain that he had come to grief and determined to find him. But he was nowhere to be seen, and in fact it was two years before his own relatives learned what had become of him. He had travelled deep into the woods and had hired with a lumber company as a lumber jack, under an assumed name, where he thought no one would find him.

This story was not known to me as I watched Lulu become more and more agitated when time passed and she was not summoned to go downstairs for the ceremony. The mistress of the house, and a young girl of eighteen who was to act as bridesmaid, kept going and coming to reassure her.

"He's been held by some accident. Don't worry, Lulu."

"It's started to snow. Maybe in his direction they're having a blizzard."

"Tomorrow you'll be a married woman and you'll laugh at taking on so nervous about everything."

Finally Mother paid a visit to the disturbed bride-to-be. Lulu, when she saw her, went to her and laid her head on Mother's shoulder. I could see that she was struggling against sobs.

"There's nothing to worry about, Lulu," Mother said. "If he's a good man, good enough for you, he'll come somehow. It's not six yet. Lots of things could have happened to keep him."

149

Lulu said nothing but she brightened after that and soon we heard sleigh bells jingling. She sped to the window and turned to catch me in her arms. "He's come, Jessie," she said. "He's here! Oh, Jessie! It's wonderful, wonderful."

I agreed with Lulu that it was wonderful, little guessing then, the degree of her anxiety.

But there were still problems to be solved; for indeed there had been an accident, and in going through a deep pitch-hole, the cutter had upset. The groom-to-be had caught his trouser leg on the end of a cutter shoe, and torn the garment from waist to ankle. Someone loaned him a pair of trousers while his promised wife performed her first wifely duty by mending the rent for him as best she could. The material was dark purple velvet corduroy and her hand smoothed it as she worked.

Soon, we heard an organ wheezing out the familiar *Wedding March* and several of the ladies, including Mother, appeared to see that all was in order for the procession to begin.

How proud I was to stand beside Lulu and to listen to the solemn words which the minister read from his black book. Lulu's glowing cheeks and her shining eyes told me better than anything else could how wonderful it must be to become a bride.

But when I accepted the honour of holding the bouquet, which was composed of red geraniums and fern with a centre formed by three white rosebuds (which I learned later were artificial since flowers could not be brought long distances in cold weather), I waited enchanted for the meeting of hands and the placing of that magical gold band which would change the nature of things for a man and a woman, so Mother had explained to me.

Mother's own wedding ring was not of clumsy width as some had been that I had seen, but a delicate thing beginning to wear thin. She sometimes had sighed and said. "I've never had it off," touching it almost reverently and with a tender look, "never since the day your father put it on," she would add.

What was the consternation of everyone, including the flustered bridegroom, when it was discovered that Lulu's wedding ring had been thrown from his pocket when the cutter had pitched its occupants into the snowdrifts.

A few whispered words passed between groom and minister and then something was slipped from hand to hand, reaching the palm of the husband-to-be in time to save the situation, and the ceremony went on.

After the nuptial kiss, the organ-playing was resumed and soon everyone was congratulating the groom and embracing the glowing Lulu.

It was midnight before we sat down to the feast, and feast it was. Even in her joy, Lulu did not forget the child who was placed beside her, sharing more deeply than she guessed, perhaps, in her happiness.

While the dancing went on and my father circled the room first with one partner and then with another, while Mother proved an able competitor, I stood watching with a kind of pleasure which I had never known. My parents were hard working and I had never before seen them participating in amusement such as this.

About two o'clock in the morning, during a dreamy waltz, while the wind whistled and the snow began to fall, the wedded couple stopped before Mother who was sitting out a dance with a black-moustached older man. She had been whirled through the room by a younger lad and was catching her breath. Lulu bent to whisper something. I was sitting beside Mother and Lulu kissed me, whispering, "I'll be back soon to see you, Jessie."

Almost immediately I lost sight of her in the revolving company and Mother smiled. "They've gone," she said, "to get ready for the honeymoon trip. They chose the right time for everybody's so busy dancing, they won't be missed."

But they were missed in a few minutes and the dancers

151

stopped and lined up before the exit from the stairs. I felt tears in my eyes, now, for this was good-bye to Lulu and I really loved her.

To my surprise the young couple foiled the wedding guests by slipping down a back stairs to the back door. Soon we heard the jingle of bells again. There was a rush to the windows. Yes, they had gone. The horse and cutter could be seen speeding down the road under the light of a late rising moon.

"That was a close shave for Lulu," my father remarked as we drove home in the early morning. "She was too nice a girl to be left in the lurch a second time. But I wonder who provided the ring?"

"She may have her own by now," Mother said. "They would look in the snowdrift going back. Somebody had to help out."

There was an evasiveness in Mother's voice. I looked up at her and she smiled into my eyes. My father turned to look at her, too. He was driving with bare hands as was his habit even in the coldest weather; now he slipped the reins into his right hand and laid his left hand over Mother's which were gloved in her lap.

"That was like you, Ma," he said and his voice had a quality of mingled tenderness and pride. "I'm glad you did it."

I was glad, too, but it seemed strange to have a Mother without a wedding ring. I may have appeared troubled, for she said quietly, later, "Don't mention this to anyone, Jessie. It's a kind of secret."

I didn't mention what Mother had done to anyone but I was glad when Lulu came back a few days afterward wearing a ring of her own. That night while Mother was sewing, she stopped several times and smoothed the worn gold band again on her hand. I knew that she was glad, too.

Epilogue

A day.
I can remember when a day
Was long enough for this and here and there,
But now – a breath of dawn, a star, and 'tis away.
I wonder as I search my memory through
For record of the hours. Where can they be?
No time ago, each one had separate meaning and a price,
By some small thing I knew
Each day from all the others. I could say:
'That was the morning Simon cut the hay
And left it drying in the sun, while I
Lay prone upon it watching clouds float by;
Or rain was falling like a mother's tears
And when your letter came, it stopped, and all
The air grew sunny and perfumed.' A small
Thing to remember; but the hours that run
Each into each, until the day is done,
And will not answer when I call the roll,
But make of life an undivided whole,
These take from life a very heavy toll.

Jessie L. Beattie